MENAPHON

AND

A MARGARITE OF AMERICA

MENAPHON

By Robert Greene

AND

A MARGARITE OF AMERICA

By Thomas Lodge

Edited by G. B. HARRISON, M.A.
Lecturer in English Literature at King's
College in the University of London

OXFORD
Basil Blackwell
1 9 2 7

INTRODUCTION

WHEN the history of taste comes to be written, not the least valuable evidence will be provided by those novels which were once popular but have lacked the universality, or the commoness, to outlive their original public; they were created to satisfy a desire and they are the direct expression of the taste of their readers. Great books survive transplanting; Shakespeare needs no reconstructed Globe or facsimile reprint of the Folio; but with the works of lesser men the reader must use his historic imagination, recreating, so far as is possible, the mood of those for whom they were first written.

Menaphon, Camillas Alarum to slumbering Euphues, in his melancholie Cell at Silexedra was entered for publication in the Stationers' Register on August 23rd, 1589, the entry reading—

Sampson Clerke Entred for his Copie, menophon Camillus allarum to slumberinge Ephewes in his melancholy cell at Silexedria. Vnder th[e h]andes of Master doctour Staller and bothe the Wardens. ... vj[d] [1]

It was printed before the end of the year and four other editions at least were printed in the next eighteen years.[2]

---

[1] *Arber's Reprint*, ii. 529.
[2] For a discussion of the bibliography of *Menaphon*, see Dr. R. B. McKerrow's edition of *The Works of Thomas Nashe*, iii. 300.

Menaphon is a typical specimen of the work of a University Wit with a sure instinct for what his public will appreciate. Greene had no high theories about his own intuitions, and he is quite frank in his intentions—'I did it for your pleasures,' he writes in his epistle 'To the Gentlemen Readers,' 'whereunto I euer aymed my thoughts'; but at the same time he was well aware of his skill in this kind of writing, and anxious that they shall not overlook its merits, but 'take a little pains to prie into my imagination'.

The University Wits at first served a very special public, and for some time they were not a little proud of the fact that they wrote not for the multitude but for a select audience of courtiers and their ladies, and gentlemen of the Inns of Court and of the two Universities who shared—as do all who have been nurtured in the old humane studies—the freemasonry of apt quotation or classical allusion. It was essentially a leisured public, valuing rather the manner than the matter in a piece of literary artistry.

But the ascendancy of the University Wits was short lived. Marlowe had already deserted them, and, to Greene's thinking, was degrading himself by writing for the public stages; for Greene and his fellows were bitterly jealous of the professional players who were growing rich on the products of poor scholars' brains. It was a losing battle, and there is an uneasy note in the verses which 'Thomas Brabine, Gent.' contributes in praise of the author—

'Players auant, you know not to delight;
Welcome sweete Shepheard worth a Schollers sight.'

Within a very short time, if indeed he had not already

done so, Greene was obliged to follow the rest and
'striue to thunder from a Stage-mans throate'; but he
did it unwillingly, being forced by his necessities, and
his bitterness was not diminished when he was con-
fronted with the early successes of that Upstart Crow
who was not even a University Man.

The preface 'To the Gentlemen Students of both
Universities' contributed by Thomas Nashe has its
place in the history of English criticism. It is the
effusion of a young man just down from the University
who is anxious to distinguish himself by breaking a
lance in the cause of poetry, and at the same time glad
of a chance to slip in a useful advertisement of his forth-
coming *Anatomie of Absurditie* under the sponsorship of
the most popular writer of the day. But he has the truth
of the matter in him when he says, 'I deeme him farre
vnworthy the name of a scholer, and so, consequently,
to sacrifice his endeuours to Art, that is not a Poet,
either in whole or in part.'

Nashe's preface and its allusions, however, belong to
literary politics. *Menaphon* itself is a good example of
the pastoral romance in Greene's earlier manner. For-
tunately he has refrained from using his pastoral form
as a cover for personalities, and has concerned himself
with telling a very pleasing story. Greene imitates both
Lyly and Sidney; he acknowledges his debt to the former on the title page, by presenting his story to 'Euphues in his Cell at Silexedra'; to the latter by placing
his scene in Arcadia. But Greene is not a mere imitator;
and he surpassed both his models. He realised that a
pastoral romance should be of reasonable length and so
avoided the interminable prolixity of the *Arcadia;* he
shared Lyly's love for parallels and fine phrases, but he

does not spoil his work by an overcurious exactitude of balance; nor does he sacrifice the story either to mere decoration or to a moral lesson. In fact Greene owes the faults of *Menaphon* to his models, the virtues are his own.

Not the least surprising quality of Greene's work is the atmosphere of purity and idyllic sweetness which appears in most of his novels and in his best plays, *Friar Bacon and Friar Bungay* and *James the Fourth;* for his vicious life in London was a byword amongst the opponents of poetry. Yet for all his loose companions Greene belonged by temperament to the serious generation of Sidney and Spenser; he was a moralist, sincerely and even morbidly religious; and it may be that in his works of fancy he tried to escape from the squalor of his brothel mates into the purer air of an Arcadia which owed not a little to the memory of those first months that he had spent in the country after his marriage with his much wronged 'Doll.'

Greene was a Norfolk man of lower middle class; Thomas Lodge his friend, and for some time his partner, came of a well-to-do city family, his father having been Lord Mayor of London in 1563.[1] He was born about 1558, and in 1571 was admitted to the Merchant Taylors' School under the famous headmaster, Richard Mulcaster. Thence he went up to Trinity College, Oxford, where he took his Bachelor's degree on July 8th, 1577. In the following spring, he became a member of Lincoln's Inn and began to study law. In 1579, when his mother died, he wrote a memorial poem, entered in the Stationers' Register on December 23rd, but no copies seem now to be in existence. In the same year he

---

[1] For a biography of Lodge, see the Memoir contributed by Sir Edmund Gosse in 1887 to the edition of Lodge, published by the Hunterian Club.

had written a reply to Gosson's *School of Abuse;* this was
suppressed by authority, presumably because he defended plays, though the pamphlet, which has survived
in spite of the censor, is not likely to have caused much
harm to anyone's morals. Gosson's abuse of the stage
was foolish enough on general grounds, but when he
spoke of the practical inconveniences to the common-
wealth he was talking sense. Lodge's counter-argu-
ments are the debating points of a young man fresh
from the University who has not yet learnt how to use
his commonplace book. He argues for instance in favour of stage playing—

'For tragedies and comedies *Donate* the gramarian
sayth, they wer inuented by lerned fathers of the old
time to no other purpose, but to yeelde prayse vnto God
for a happy haruest, or plentifull yeere, and that thys is
trewe the name of Tragedye doeth importe, for if you
consider whence it came, you shall perceiue (as *Iodocus
Badius* reporteth) that it drewe his original of *Tragos*,
Hircus, and *Ode*, *Cantus* (so called) for that the actors
thereof had in rewarde for theyr labour, a Gotes skynne
fylled wyth wyne. You see then that the fyrste matter
of Tragedies was to giue thankes and prayses to God,
and a gratefull prayer of the countrymen for a happye
haruest, and this I hope was not discommendable. I
knowe you will iudge is farthest from abuse, but to
wade farther, thys fourme of inuention being found out,
as the dayes wherein it was used did decay, and the
world grew to more perfection, so y^t witt of the younger
sorte became more riper, for they leauing this fourme,
inuented an other, in the which they altered the nature
but not ye name: for for sonnets in prayse of ye gods,
they did set forth the sower fortune of many exiles, the

miserable fal of haples princes, The ruinous decay of many countryes, yet not content with this, they present-ed the liues of *Satyers*, So that they might wiselye vnder the abuse of that name, discouer the follies of many theyr folish fellow citesens, and those monsters were then, as our parasites are now adayes; such, as with pleasure reprehended abuse.'[1]

The *Reply* is innocent of any attempt at literary criti-cism.

Lodge's father died in 1583, and if *An Allarum against Vsurers* which was entered on November 4th in that year is in any way autobiographical, Lodge seems to have suffered the fate not uncommon to those who pawn their inheritance with a moneylender. The careers of the unfortunate victims of the broker are indeed very similar to what is known of Lodge's early life, though the general tone of the work does not suggest that Lodge was trying to make capital out of his own back-slidings. The *Alarum* is valuable not merely as an economic document but also as being the most import-ant exposure of a social abuse between Harman's *Ca-veat for Common Cursetors* (1566) which showed up the professional beggars of the road and Greene's arraign-ment of the professional rascals of the city in his Conny Catching pamphlets (1591-2).

For the next five years Lodge seems to have pub-lished nothing. In 1589 was printed *Scylla's Metamor-phosis*, 'with sundry other most absolute Poems and Sonnets,' in which he set a fashion followed by Shakes-peare in *Venus and Adonis*. During these years Lodge made two voyages to the West Indies with Thomas

---

[1] *A Reply to Stephen Gosson's Schoole of Abuse*, Hunterian Club, 1879, page 35.

Cavendish, in which he wrote two at least of his best works, *Rosalynde* (published 1590) and *A Margarite of America* (published 1596), and perhaps others as well, for between 1589 and 1596 several volumes were printed, including the plays, *The Wounds of Civil War* and *A Looking Glass for London* (written in collaboration with Greene), and *A Fig for Momus*, the first batch of formal Elizabethan verse satire; though Lodge's satires are mild and general compared with the vituperation of his successors, Donne, Hall and Marston.

It is probable that by this time he had turned Catholic, and whether for politic reasons or because in (Anthony à Wood's words) 'his mind growing serious, he studied Physick, for the improvement of which he travelled beyond the seas, took the degree of Doctor of that faculty at *Avenion* [Avignon], returned and was incorporated in the University in the latter end of Qu. *Elizabeth*. Afterwards settling in *London* he practised it, being much frequented for his success in it, especially by the R. Catholicks (of which number he was by many suspected to be one) and was as much cried up to his last for Physick, as he was in his younger days for his poetical fancy.'[1]

Lodge's later publications were more weighty. He translated the works of Josephus in 1602, and in 1603, when the plague was raging in London, he wrote *A Treatise of the Plague*, an enlightened work, wherein he advocates the building of an isolation hospital for London, and lays down most sensible rules for the sanitary measures to be taken in infected houses. In 1613 he translated the moral and physical works of Seneca. He died of the plague in 1625.

[1] *Athenæ Oxonienses*, 1691, i. 424.

A Margarite of America, is perhaps the best of Lodge's fanciful works, though not so well known as *Rosalynde*, which has been more studied because it was the original source of Shakespeare's *As You Like It*, and has therefore suffered somewhat from unfair competition. Yet it is likely that Shakespeare was familiar with *A Margarite from America* too, since several reminiscences from it occur in his plays which seem to be too close to be coincidence. Protomachus' farewell counsels to Arsinous (pp.129-132) are very similar to the 'few precepts' which Polonius bestows upon Laertes, and the poem *Humanæ Miseriæ Discursus* (page 120) taken with Arsadachus' remorseful groan, 'True it is that Plutarch saith that life is a stage play which euen to the last hath no decorum,' seem to be echoed in 'All the world's a stage.'

But Lodge deserves to be read for his own worth and not because a greater than he took some of his jewels and reset them. His elaborate tapestries still have colour, freshness and an intricate beauty which is reminiscent of some of the best paintings of Rosetti, but their worth lies in their curious artistry, and not in their utility either as psychological studies or as specimens of plot construction. The very real charm of *Menaphon* and *A Margarite of America* does not appear until they are read aloud, as they were meant to be read, with each sweet period rolled a little delicately round the palate; and preferably on a summer's day under a large oak tree.

King's College,   G. B. HARRISON.
University of London.

MENAPHON
Camillas alarum to
slumbering Euphues, in his
melancholie Cell at Si-
lexedra.

VVherein are deciphered the variable effects
of Fortune, the wonders of Loue, the tri-
umphes of inconstant Time.

Displaying in sundrie concepted passions (figu-
red in a continuate Historie) the Trophees that
Vertue carrieth triumphant, maugre
the wrath of Enuie, or the resolution of Fortune.

A worke worthie the youngest eares
for pleasure, or the grauest censures
for principles.

Robertus Greene in Artibus magister.

Omne tulit punctum.

LONDON
Printed by T. O. for Sampson Clarke,
and are to be sold behinde the Royall Exchange. 1589.

To the right Worshipfull and ver-
tuous Ladie, the Ladie Hales, wife to the late
deceased Sir Iames Hales; Robert Greene
wisheth increase of Worship and vertue.

WHEN *Alexander* (right worshipfull) was troubled
with hottest feuers, *Phillip* the phisition broght
him the coldest potions; extreams haue ther Antidotes,
and the driest melancholy hath a moistest sanguin; wise
Hortenzia midst hir greatest dumpes; either playd with
hir Children, or read some pleasant verses: such as sorrow hath pinched mirth must cure. This considered;
hearing (madam) of the passions your Ladiship hath
vttered a late for the losse of your husband, a Knight in
life worshipfull, vertuous, and full of honourable
thoghts; discouering by such passionate sorowes the
patterne of a louing and vertuous wife, whose ioyes
liued in hir husbands weale, and ended with his life, I
thought it my dutie to write this pastorall historie, con-
teyning the manifolde iniuries of fortune, that both
your Ladiship might see her inconstant follies, and
beare hir frownes with more patience, and when your
dumpes were most deepe, then to looke on this little
treatise for recreation: wherein there be as well humors
to delight, as discourses to aduise. Which if your Ladi-

1

ship shall vouch to accept, couering my presumption and faultes which your wonted courtesie; I haue the wished end of my labors. In which hope reﬆing, I commit your Ladiship to the Almightie.

Yours in all humble seruice,

Robert Greene.

To the Gentlemen Readers, health.

*I*T *fareth with mee Gentlemen, as with* Batillus *the ouer bold poet of* Rome, *that at euerie winke of* Cæsar *would deliuer vp an hundred verses, though neuer a one plausible, thinking the Emperours smile a priuiledge for his ignorance: so I hauing your fauor in letting passe my Pamphlets, feare not to trouble your patience with many works, and such as if* Batillus *had liued; hee might well haue subscribed his name to. But resting vpon your fauors I haue thus farre aduentured to let you see* Camillas alarum *to* Euphues, *who thought it necessarie not to let* Euphues *censure to* Philautus, *passe without requitall. If Gentlemen you finde my ſtile either* magis humile *in some place, or more* sublime *in another, if you finde darke Ænigmaes or ſtrange conceipts as if* Sphinx *on the one side, and* Roscius *on the other were playing the wagges; thinke the metaphors are well ment, and that I did it for your pleasures, whereunto I euer aymed my thoughts: and desire you to take a little paines to prie into my imagination. Wherein if you shall reſt mine, I shall euer as I haue done reſt yours; and so I bid you farewell.*

3

To the Gentlemen Students of both
Vniuersities.

CVRTEOUS and wise, whose iudgements (not entangled with enuie) enlarge the deserts of the
Learned by your liberall censures; vouchsafe to welcome your scholler-like Shepheard with such Vniuersitie entertainement, as either the nature of your bountie, or the custome of your common ciuilitie may affoord.
To you he appeales that knew him *ab extrema pueritia*,
whose *placet* he accounts the *plaudite* of his paines;
thinking his daie labour was not altogether lauisht *sine
linea*, if there be anie thing of all in it, that doth *olere
atticum* in your estimate. I am not ignorant how eloquent our gowned age is growen of late; so that euerie
mœchanicall mate abhorres the english he was borne
too, and plucks with a solemne periphrasis, his *vt vales*
from the inkhorne: which I impute not so much to the
perfection of arts, as to the seruile imitation of vain-
glorious tragœdians, who contend not so seriouslie to
excell in action, as to embowell the clowdes in a speach
of comparison; thinking themselues more than initiated
in poets immortalitie, if they but once get *Boreas* by the
beard, and the heauenlie bull by the deaw-lap. But here-
in I cannot so fully bequeath them to follie, as their
idiote art-masters, that intrude theseules to our eares as
the alcumists of eloquence; who (moūted on the stage
of arrogance) think to outbraue better pens with the
swelling bumbast of a bragging blanke verse. Indeed it

4

may be the ingrafted ouerflow of some kilcow conceipt, that ouerclioieth their imagination with a more than drunken resolution, beeing not extemporall in the inuention of anie other meanes to vent their manhood, commits the disgestion of their cholerick incumbrances, to the spacious volubilitie of a drumming decasillabon. Mongst this kinde of men that repose eternitie in the mouth of a player, I can but ingrosse some deepe read Grammarians, who hauing no more learning in their scull, than will serue to take vp a commoditie; nor Art in their brain, than was nourished in a seruing mans idlenesse, will take vpon them to be the ironicall censors of all, when God and Poetrie doth know, they are the simplest of all. To leaue these to the mercie of their mother tongue, that feed on nought but the crummes that fal from the translators trencher, I come (sweet friend) to thy *Arcadian Menaphon*; whose attire though not so statelie, yet comelie, dooth entitle thee aboue all other, to that *temperatum dicendi genus*, which *Tullie* in his *Orator* tearmeth true eloquence. Let other men (as they please) praise the mountaine that in seauen yeares brings foorth a mouse, or the Italionate pen, that of a packet of pilfries, affoordeth the presse a pamphlet or two in an age, and then in disguised arraie, vaunts *Ouids* and *Plutarchs* plumes as their owne; but giue me the man, whose extemporall vaine in anie humor, will excell our greatest Art-masters deliberate thoughts; whose inuention quicker than his eye, will challenge the proudest Rethoritian, to the contention of like perfection, with like expedition. What is he amongst Students so simple, that cannot bring forth (*tandem aliquando*) some or other thing singular, sleeping betwixt euerie sentence? Was it not *Maros* xij. yeares toyle, that so famed

his xij. *Æneidos?* Or *Peter Ramus* xvj. yeares paines,
that so praised his pettie Logique? Howe is it then, out
drowping wits should so wonder at an exquisite line,
that was his masters day labour? Indeede I must needes
say, the descending yeares from the Philosophers *Athens*,
haue not been supplied with such present Orators, as
were able in anie English vaine to be eloquent of their
owne, but either they must borow inuention of *Ariosto*,
and his Countreymen, take vp choyce of words by exchange in *Tullies Tusculane*, and the Latine Historio-
graphers store-houses; similitudes, nay whole sheetes
and tractacts *verbatim*, from the plentie of *Plutarch* and
Plinie; and to conclude, their whole methode of writing,
from the libertie of Comical fictions, that haue succeed-
ed to our Rethoritians, by a second imitation: so that,
well may the Adage, *Nil dictum quod non dictum prius*,
bee the most iudiciall estimate, of our latter Writers.
But the hunger of our vnsatiate humorists, beeing such
as it is, readie to swallowe all draffe without indiffer-
ence, that insinuates it selfe to their senses vnder the
name of delight, imployes oft times manie thredbare
witts, to emptie their inuention of their Apish deuices,
and talke most superficiallie of Pollicie, as those that
neuer ware gowne in the Vniuersitie; wherein they re-
niue the olde saide Adage, *Sus Mineruam*, and cause the
wiser to quippe them with *Asinus ad Lyram*. Would
Gentlemen and riper iudgements admit my motion of
moderation in a matter of follie, I wold perswade them
to phisicke their faculties of seeing and hearing, as the
Sabæans doo their dulled senses with smelling; who (as
Strabo reporteth) ouer-cloyed with such odoriferous
sauours, as the naturall encrease of their Countrey,
(Balsamum, Amomum, with Myrrhe and Franken-

cense) sends foorth, refresh their nosthrills with the vn-
sauorie sent, of the pitchie slime, that *Euphrates* casts
vp, and the contagious fumes of Goates beardes burnt;
so woulde I haue them, beeing surfetted vnawares with
the sweete sacietie of eloquence, which the lauish of our
copious Language maie procure, to vse the remedie of
contraries; and recreate their rebated witts, not as they
did, with the senting of slyme or Goates beardes burnt,
but with the ouer-seeing of that *sublime dicendi genus*,
which walkes abroad for wast paper in each seruing
mans pocket, and the otherwhile perusing of our
Gothamists barbarisme; so shoulde the opposite comparison of *Puritie*, expell the infection of absurditie; and
their ouer-rackte Rhethorique, bee the Ironicall recreation of the Reader. But so farre discrepant is the
idle vsage of our vnexperienst punies from this pre-
scription, that a tale of Ihon a Brainfords will, and the
vnluckie furmentie, wil be as soon interteined into their
libraries, as the best poeme that euer *Tasso* eternisht:
which being the effect of an vndescerning iudgement,
makes drosse as valuable as gold, and losse as welcome
as gaine, the Glow-worme mentioned in *Æsops* fables,
namelie the apes follie, to be mistaken for fire, when as
God wot poore soules, they haue nought but their toyle
for their heate, their paines for their sweate, and (to
bring it to our english prouerbe) their labour for their
trauaile. Wherein I can but resemble them to the Pan-
ther, who is so greedie of mens excrements; that if they
be hangd vp in a vessell higher than his reach, he
sooner killeth himselfe with the ouer-stretching of his
windlesse bodie, than he wil cease from his intended
enterprise. Oft haue I obserued what I now set downe;
a secular wit that hath liued all daies of his life by what

doo you lacke, to bee more iudiciall in matters of conceit, than our quadrant crepundios, that spit *ergo* in the
mouth of euerie one they meete: yet those and these are
so affectionate to dogged detracting, as the moſt poy-
sonous *Pasquil*, anie durtie mouthed *Martin*, or *Momus*
euer composed, is gathered vp with greedinesse before
it fall to the ground, and bought at the deereſt though
they smell of the friplers lauander halfe a yeere after:
for I know not how the minde of the meaneſt is fedde
with this follie, that they impute singularitie, to him
that slanders priuelie, and count it a great peece of arte
in an inkhorne man, in anie tapſterlie tearmes whatsoeuer, to oppose his superiours to enuie. I will not denie
but in scholler-like matters of controuersie, a quicker
ſtile may passe as commendable; and that a quippe to
an asse is as good as a goad to an oxe: but when an ir-
regular idiot, that was vp to the eares in diuinitie, before
euer he met with *probabile* in the Vniuersitie, shall leaue
pro et contra before he can scarcely pronounce it, and
come to correct Common weales, that neuer heard of
the name of Magiſtrate before he came to *Cambridge*, it
is no meruaile if euery alehouse vaunt the table of the
world turned vpside down; since the childe beats his
father, and the asse whippes his maſter. But leaſt I
might seeme with these night crowes, *Nimis curiosus in
aliena republica*, I'le turne backe to my firſt text, of ſtud-
ies of delight; and talke a little in friendship with a few
of our triuiall translators. It is a cõmon practise now a
daies amongſt a sort of shifting companions, that runne
through euery arte and thriue by none, to leaue the
trade of *Nouerint* whereto they were borne, and busie
themselues with the indeuors of Art, that could scarcelie
latinize their necke-verse if they should haue neede;

yet English *Seneca* read by candle light yeeldes manie
good sentences, as *Bloud is a begger*, and so foorth: and
if you intreate him faire in a frostie morning, he will
affoord you whole *Hamlets*, I should say handfulls of
tragical speaches. But ô griefe! *tempus edax rerum*,
what's that will last alwaies? The sea exhaled by droppes
will in continuance be drie, and *Seneca* let bloud line by
line and page by page, at length must needes die to our
stage: which makes his famisht followers to imitate the
Kidde in *Æsop*, who enamored with the Foxes new
fangles, forsooke all hopes of life to leape into a new
occupation; and these men renowncing all possibilities
of credit or estimation, to intermeddle with Italian
translations: wherein how poorelie they haue plodded,
(as those that are neither prouenzall men, nor are able
to distinguish of Articles,) let all indifferent Gentlemen
that haue trauailed in that tongue, discerne by their
twopenie pamphlets: and no meruaile though their
home-born mediocritie be such in this matter; for what
can be hoped of those, that thrust *Elisium* into hell, and
haue not learned so long as they haue liued in the
spheares, the iust measure of the Horizon without an
hexameter. Sufficeth them to bodge vp a blanke verse
with ifs and ands, and other while for recreation after
their candle stuffe, hauing starched their beardes most
curiouslie, to make a peripateticall path into the inner
parts of the Citie, and spend two or three howers in
turning ouer French *Doudie*, where they attract more
infection in one minute, than they can do eloquence all
dayes of their life, by conuersing with anie Authors of
like argument. But least in this declamatorie vaine, I
should condemne all and commend none, I will pro-
pound to your learned imitation, those men of import,

that haue laboured with credit in this laudable kinde of Translation; In the forefront of whom, I cannot but place that aged Father *Erasmus*, that inuested most of our Greeke Writers, in the roabes of the auncient *Romaines*; in whose traces, *Philip Melancthon*, *Sadolet*, *Plantine*, and manie other reuerent Germaines insisting, haue reedified the ruines of our decayed Libraries, and merueilouslie inriched the Latine tongue with the expence of their toyle. Not long after, their emulation beeing transported into *England*, euerie priuate Scholler, *William Turner*, and who not, beganne to vaunt their smattering of Latine, in English Impressions. But amongst others in that Age, Sir *Thomas Eliots* elegance did seuer it selfe from all equalls, although Sir *Thomas Moore* with his Comicall wit, at that instant was not altogether idle: yet was not Knowledge fullie confirmed in hir Monarchie amongst vs, till that most famous and fortunate Nurse of all learning, Saint *Iohns* in *Cambridge*, that at that time was as an Vniuersitie within it selfe; shining so farre aboue all other Houses, Halls, and Hospitalls whatsoeuer, that no Colledge in the Towne, was able to compare with the tythe of her Students; hauing (as I haue hearde graue men of credite report) more candles light in it, euerie Winter Morning before fowre of the clocke, than the fowre of clocke bell gaue stroakes; till Shee (I saie) as a pittying Mother, put too her helping hande, and sent from her fruitefull wombe, sufficient Schollers, both to support her owne weale, as also to supplie all other inferiour foundations defects, and namelie that royall erection of *Trinitie Colledge*, which the Vniuersitie Orator, in an Epistle to the Duke of *Somerset*, aptlie tearmed *Colona diducta*, from the Suburbes of *Saint Iohns*. In which

extraordinarie conception, *vno partu in rempublicam pro-
diere*, the Exchequer of eloquence Sir *Ihon Cheeke*, a
man of men, supernaturally traded in al tongues, Sir
Ihon Mason, Doctor *Watson*, *Redman*, *Aschame*, *Grin-
dall*, *Leuer*, *Pilkington*: all which, haue either by their
priuate readings, or publique workes, repurged the
errors of Artes, expelde from their puritie, and set before our eyes, a more perfect Methode of Studie. But
howe ill their preceptes haue prospered with our idle
Age, that leaue the fountaines of sciences, to follow the
riuers of Knowledge, their ouer-fraught Studies, with
trifling Compendiaries maie testifie: for I knowe not
howe it comes to passe, by the doating practise of our
Diuinitie dunces, that striue to make their Pupills pul-
pet men, before they are reconciled to *Priscian*: but
those yeares, which shoulde bee employed in *Aristotle*,
are expired in Epitomes; and well too, they maye haue
so much Catechisme vacation, to rake vp a little refuse
Philosophie. And heere could I enter into a large fielde
of inuectiue, against our abiect abbreuiations of Artes,
were it not growen to a newe fashion amongst our Na-
tion, to vaunt the pride of contraction in euerie manuarie action: in so much, that the *Pater noster*, which was
woont to fill a sheete of paper, is written in the compasse of a pennie: whereupon one merelie affirmed, that
prouerb to be deriued, *No pennie, no pater noster*; which
their nice curtalling, puts me in mind of the custome of
the *Scythians*, who if they be at any time distressed with
famin, take in their girdles shorter, and swaddle themselues streighter, to the intent no *vacuum* beeing left in
their intrayles, hunger should not so much tirannnize
ouer their stomacks; euen so these men opprest with a
greater penurie of Art, do pound their capacitie in bar-

ren Compendiums, and bound their base humors, in
the beggerly ſtraites of a hungry Analysis, leaſt longing
after that *infinitum* which the pouertie of their conceit
cannot compasse, they sooner yeeld vp their youth to
deſtinie, than their heart to vnderſtanding. How is it
then, such bungling practitioners in principles, shuld
euer profite the Common wealth by their negligent
paines, who haue no more cunning in Logique or
Dialogue Latine, than appertains to the literall con-
ſtruction of either; neuerthelesse it is daily apparant to
our domeſticall eyes, that there is none so forward to
publish their imperfections, either in the trade of glose
or translations, as those that are more vnlearned than
ignorance, and lesse conceiuing than infants. Yet dare I
not impute absurditie to all of that societie, though
some of them haue set their names to their simplicitie.
Who euer my priuate opinion condemneth as faultie,
Maſter *Gascoigne* is not to bee abridged of his deserued
eſteeme, who firſt beate the path to that perfection
which our beſt Poets haue aspired too since his departure; whereto he did ascend by comparing the Italian
with the English, as *Tullie* did *Græca cum Latinis*. Neither was Maſter *Turbeuile* the worſt of his time, although in translating he attributed too much to the
necessitie of rime. And in this page of praise, I cannot
omit aged *Arthur Golding*, for his induſtrious toile in
Englishing *Ouids Metamorphosis*, besides manie other
exquisite editions of Diuinitie, turned by him out of the
French tongue into our own. Maſter *Phaer* likewise is
not to be forgot in regard of his famous *Virgil*, whose
heauēly verse had it not bin blemisht by his hautie
thoghts *England* might haue long insulted in his wit,
and *corrigat qui poteſt* haue been subscribed to his

workes. But fortune the Miſtres of change with a pitying compassion, respecting Maſter *Stanihurſts* praise,
would that *Phaer* shoulde fall that hee might rise,
whose heroicall Poetrie infired, I should say inspired,
with an hexameter furie, recalled to life, what euer
hissed barbarisme, hath bin buried this hundred yeare;
and reuiued by his ragged quill, such carterlie varietie,
as no hodge plowman in a countrie, but would haue
held as the extremitie of clownerie; a patterne whereof,
I will propounde to your iudgements, as neere as I can,
being parte of one of his descriptions of a tempeſt,
which is thus

Then did he make, heauens vault to rebounde, with rounce
  robble hobble
Of ruffe raffe roaring, with thwick thwack thurlery bounc-
  ing

Which ſtrange language of the firmament neuer subiect before to our common phrase, makes vs that are not
vsed to terminate heauens moueings, in the accents of
to any voice, eſteeme of their triobulare interpreter, as of
some Thrasonicall huffe snuffe, for so terrible was his ſtile,
all milde eares, as would haue affrighted our peaceable
Poets, from intermedling hereafter, with that quarrel-
ling kinde of verse; had not sweete Maſter *France* by
his excellent translation of Maſter *Thomas Watsons*
sugred *Amintas*, animated their dulled spirits, to such
high witted endeuors. But I knowe not how, their ouer
timerous cowardise, hath ſtoode in awe of enuie, that no
man since him, durſt imitate any of the worſte, of those
Romane wonders in english, which makes me thinke,
that either the louers of mediocritie, are verie many, or
that the number of good Poets, are very small: and in

trueth, (Master *Watson* except, whom I mentioned before) I knowe not almost any of late dayes that hath
shewed himselfe singular in any special Latine Poëm,
whose *Amintas*, and translated *Antigone* may march in
equipage of honour, with any of our ancient Poets. I
will not say but wee had a *Haddon* whose pen would
haue challenged the Lawrell from *Homer*, together with
Carre, that came as nere him, as *Virgil* to *Theocritus*.
But *Tho. Newton* with his *Leyland*, and *Gabriell Haruey*,
with two or three other, is almost all the store, that is
left vs at this hower. Epitaphers, and position Poets
haue wee more than a good many, that swarme like
Crowes to a dead carcas, but flie like Swallows in the
VVinter, from any continuate subiect of witte. The
efficient whereof, I imagine to issue, from the vpstart
discipline, of our reformatorie Churchmen, who account wit vanitie, and poetrie impietie; whose error,
although the necessitie of Philosophie might confute,
which lies couched most closely vnder darke fables pro-
funditie, yet I had rather referre it, as a disputatiue plea
to diuines, than set it downe as a determinate position,
in my vnexperienst opinion. But how euer their dissen-
tious iudgements, should decree in their afternoone
sessions of *an sit*, the priuat trueth, of my discouered
Creede in this controuersie is this, that as that beast,
was thought scarce worthie to bee sacrifised, to the
Ægiptian *Epaphus*, who had not some or other blacke
spotte on his skinne: so I deeme him farre vnworthie of
the name of a scholler, and so consequentlie, to sacrifice
his endeuors to art, that is not a Poet, either in whole or
in a parte and here peraduenture, some desperate quip-
per, will canuaze my proposed comparison *plus vltra*,
reconciling the allusion of the blacke spot, to the blacke

pot; which makes our Poets vndermeale Muses so
mutinous, as euerie ſtanzo they pen after dinner, is full
poynted with a ſtabbe. Which their dagger drunkennesse, although it might be excused, with *Tam Marti
quam Mercurio*, yet will I couer it as well as I may, with
that prouerbiall *fœcundi calices*, that might wel haue
been doore keeper, to the kanne of *Silenus*, when nod-
ding on his Asse trapt with iuie, hee made his moiſt
nosecloth, the pausing intermedium, twixt euerie nappe.
Let frugale scholares, and fine fingerd nouices, take
their drinke by the ownce, and their wine by the halpe-
worthes, but it is for a Poet, to examine the pottle
pottes, and gage the bottome of whole gallons; *qui bene
vult* ποιειν, *debet ante* πίνειν. A pot of blew burning ale,
with a fierie flaming toſt, is as good as *Pallas* with the
nine Muses on *Pernassus* top: without the which, in
vaine may they crie; ô thou my muse inspire mee with
some pen, when they want certaine liquid sacrifice, to
rouze her foorth her denne. Pardon me Gentlemen,
though somewhat merely I glaunce, at their imoderate
follie, who affirme that no man can write with conceit,
except he take counsell of the cup: nor would I haue
you thinke, that *Theonino dente*, I arme my ſtile againſt
all, since I doo knowe the moderation of many Gentlemen of that ſtudie, to be so farre from infamie, as their
verse from equalitie: whose sufficiencie, were it as well
seene into, by those of higher place, as it wanders
abroade vnrewarded, in the mouthes of vngratefull
monſters, no doubte but the remembrance, of *Mœcenas*
liberalitie, extended to *Maro*, and men of like qualitie,
would haue lefte no memorie to that prouerb of pouertie, *Si nihil attuleris, ibis Homere foras*. Tut saies our
English Italians, the fineſt witts our Climate sends

foorth, are but drie braind doltes, in comparison of other countries: whome if you interrupt with *redde rationem*, they will tell you of *Petrache*, *Tasso*, *Celiano*, with an infinite number of others; to whome if I should oppose *Chaucer*, *Lidgate*, *Gower*, with such like, that liued vnder the tirranie of ignorance, I do think their beſt louers, would bee much discontented, with the collation of contraries, if I should write ouer al their heads, Haile fellow well met. One thing I am sure of, that each of these three, haue vaunted their meeters, with as much admiration in English, as euer the proud-eſt *Arioſto*, did his verse in Italian. What should I come to our court, where the otherwhile vacations of our grauer Nobilitie, are prodigall of more pompous wit, and choyce of words, than euer tragick *Tasso* could attaine too: but as for paſtorall Poëmes, I will not make the comparison, leaſt our countrimens credit should bee discountenanſt by the contention, who although they cannot fare, with such inferior facilitie, yet I knowe would carrie the bucklers full easilie, from all forreine brauers, if their *subiectum circa quod*, should sauor of any thing haughtie: and should the challenge of deepe con-ceit, be intruded by any forreiner, to bring our english wits, to the tutchſtone of Arte, I would preferre, diuine Maſter *Spencer*, the miracle of wit to bandie line for line for my life, in the honor of *England*, gainſt *Spaine*, *France*, *Italie*, and all the worlde. Neither is he, the only swallow of our summer, (although *Apollo*, if his *Tripos* were vp again would pronounce him his *Socrates*) but he being forborne, there are extant about *London*, many moſt able men, to reuiue Poetrie, though it were exe-cuted ten thousand times, as in *Platos*, so in Puritanes common wealth; as for example *Mathew Roydon*, *Thom-*

as *Atchelow* and *George Peele*, the first of whome, as hee
hath shewed himselfe singular, in the immortall Epi-
taph of his beloued *Astrophel*, besides many other most
absolute comicke inuentions (made more publique by
euerie mans praise, than they can bee by my speache) so
the second, hath more than once or twise manifested,
his deepe witted, schollership in places of credit; and
for the last, thogh not the least of them all, I dare commend him to all that know him, as the chiefe supporter
of pleasance nowe liuing, the *Atlas* of Poetrie, and *pri-
mus verborum Artifex:* whose first encrease, the Ar-
raignement of *Paris*, might plead to your opinions, his
pregnant dexteritie of wit, and manifold varietie of inuention; wherein (*me iudice*) hee goeth a step beyond all
that write. Sundrie other sweete Gentlemen I know,
that haue vaunted their pens in priuate deuices, and
trickt vp a companie of taffata fooles with their feathers,
whose beautie if our Poets had not peecte with the supply of their periwigs, they might haue antickt it vntill
this time vp and downe the countrey with the King of
Fairies, and dinde euerie daie at the pease porredge ordinarie with *Delphrigus*. But *Tolossa* hath forgot that it
was sometime sackt, and beggers that euer they caried
their fardles on footback: and in truth no meruaile,
when as the deserued reputation of one *Roscius*, is of
force to inrich a rabble of counterfets; yet let subiects
for all their insolence, dedicate a *De profundis* euerie
morning to the preseruation of their *Cæsar*, least their
encreasing indignities returne them ere long to their
iugling to mediocrity, and they bewaile in weeping
blankes the wane of their Monarchie.

As Poetrie hath beene honoured in those her forenamed
professors, so it hath not beene any whit disparaged by

c

William Warners absolute *Albions*. And heere Authoritie hath a full point: in whose reuerence insisting, I
cease to expose to your sport the picture of those Pam-
phleters, and Poets, that make a patrimonie of *In speech*
and more then a younger brothers inheritance of their
Abcie. Reade fauourably, to incourage me in the first-
lings of my folly, and perswade your selues, I will perse-
cute those idiots and their heires vnto the third generation, that haue made Art bankerout of her ornaments,
and sent Poetry a begging vp and downe the Countrey.
It may be, my *Anatomie* of *Absurdities* may acquaint you
ere long with my skill in Surgerie, wherein the diseases
of Arte more merrily discouered may make our maimed
Poets out together their blankes vnto the building of an
Hospitall.

If you chance to meete it in *Paules*, shaped in a new
suite of similitudes, as if like the eloquent apprentice of
Plutarch, it were propped at seuen yeeres end in double
apparell, thinke his master hath fulfilled couenants, and
onely cancelled the Indentures of dutie. If I please, I
will thinke my ignorance indebted vnto you that
applaud it: if not, what rests, but that I be ex-
cluded from your courtesie, like
Apocrypha from your Bibles?

How euer, yours euer,
Thomas Nash.

🖋 In laudem Authoris,
Distichon amoris.

*D*ELICIOUS *words, the life of wanton wit,*
  That doo enspire our soules with sweete content;
Why haue your father Hermes *thought it fit*
  My eyes should surfet by my hearts consent?

Full twentie Summers haue I fading seene,
  And twentie Floras *in their golden guise:*
Yet neuer viewd I such a pleasant Greene
  As this, whose garnisht gleades, compare denies.

Of all the flowers a Lillie *once I lou'd,*
  Whose labouring beautie brancht it selfe abroade;
But now old age his glorie hath remoud,
  And Greener obiectes are my eyes aboade.

No countrey to the downes of Arcadie,
  Where Aganippes *euer springing wells*
Doo moyst the meades with bubling melodie;
  And makes me muse, what more in Delos *dwelles;*

There feedes our Menaphons *celestiall Muse,*
  There makes his pipe his pastorall reporte;
Which strained now a note aboue his vse,
  Foretels, he'le nere more chaunt of Choas *sporte.*

Reade all that list, and reade till you mislike;
  Condemne who can, so enuie be no iudge:
No reede can swell more higher, lesse it shrike.
  Robin *thou hast done well, care not who grudge.*

HENRIE VPCHEAR Gentleman.

Thomas Brabine Gent.

in praise of the Author.

*C*OME *foorth you witts that vaunt the pompe of speach,*
And striue to thunder from a Stage-mans throate:
View Menaphon *a note beyond your reach*;
  Whose sight will make your drumming descant doate:
Players auant, you know not to delight;
Welcome sweete Shepheard, worth a Schollers sight.

Smirna *is drie, and* Helicon *exhal'd,*
  Caballian *founts haue left their springing sourse,*
Parnassus *with his Lawrell stands appal'd*;
  And yet His *Muse keepes on her wonted course:*
Wonted said I? I wrong his paines too much,
Since that his pen before brought foorth none such.

One writes of loue, and wanders in the aire;
  Another stands on tearmes of trees and stones:
When heauens compare yeeldes but the praise of faire,
  And christall can describe but flesh and bones:
Yet countrey swaynes, whose thoughts are faith and troth,
Will shape sweete words of wooll and russet cloth.

Mongst whom if I my Tityrus *should chuse,*
  Whose warbling tunes might wanton out my woes;
To none more oftner would my solace vse,
  Than to his Pastoralls their mortall foes.
Sweete verse, sweete prose, how haue you pleasde my vaine?
Be thou still Greene, *whiles others glorie waine.*

FINIS.

Arcadia.

The reports of the Shepheards.

AFTER that the wrath of mightie *Ioue*, had wrapt *Arcadia* with noysome pestilence, in so much that the ayre yeelding preiudiciall sauors, seemd to be peremptory in some fatall resolution, *Democles* soueraigne and King of that famous Continent pitying the sinister accidents of his people, being a man as iust in his censures as royall in his possessions, as carefull for the weale of his country, as the continuance of his diadem, thinking that vnpeopled Cities were Corasiues to Princes consciences, that the strength of his subiects was the sinnews of his dominions, and that euery crowne, must conteyne a care, not onely to winne honour by forrayne conquests, but in mainteining dignitie with ciuill and domestical insights: *Democles* grounding his arguments vpon these premisses, coueting to be counted *Pater Patriæ*, calling a Parliament together, whether all his Nobilitie incited by summons made their repaire, elected two of his chiefe Lordes to passe vnto *Delphos*, at *Apollos* Oracle to heare the fatall sentence, either of their future miserie or present remedie. They hauing their charge, posting from *Arcadia* to the *Tripos* where *Pithia* sate, the sacred Nymph that deliuered out *Apollos Dylonimas*, offering as their manner is their orizons and presents, as wel to intreate by deuotion, as to perswade by boûtie, they had returned from *Apollo* this doome.

When Neptune *riding on the Southerne seas*
   shall from the bosome of his Lemman yeeld
Th'arcadian *wonder, men and Gods to please:*
   Plentie in pride shall march amidst the field,
      Dead men shall warre, and vnborne babes shall
      frowne,
      And with their fawchens hew their foemen downe.

When Lambes haue Lions for their surest guide,
   and Planets rest vpon th'arcadian *hills:*
When swelling seas haue neither ebbe nor tide,
   When equall bankes the Ocean margine fills.
      Then looke Arcadians *for a happie time,*
      And sweete content within your troubled Clyme.

No sooner had *Pithia* deliuered this scroll to the
Lordes of *Arcadie*, but they departed and brought it to
Democles, who causing the oracle to be read amongst his
distressed commons, found the *Delphian* censure more
full of doubts to amaze, than fraught with hope to comfort; thinking rather that the angrie God sent a peremp-
torie presage of ruine, thã a probable ambiguitie to
applaud any hope of remedie: yet loath to haue his carefull subiects fall into the balefull laborinth of despaire,
Democles began to discourse vnto them, that the inter-
preters of *Apollos* secretes, were not the conceipts of
humane reason, but the successe of long expected
euents; that Comets did portend at the first blaze, but
tooke effect in the dated bosome of the destinies; that
oracles were foretold at the *Delphian* Caue, but were
shapte out and finished in the Counsell house. With
such perswasiue arguments *Democles* appeased the distressed thoughtes of his doubtful countrimen, and com-

manded by proclamation that no man should prie into
the quiddities of *Apollos* answere, least sundrie censures
of his diuine secrecie, shoulde trouble *Arcadia* with
some sodaine mutinie. The King thus smoothing the
heate of his cares, rested a melancholy man in his
Courts; hiding vnder his head the double faced figure
of *Ianus*, as well to cleare the skies of other men's conceiptes with smiles, as to furnish out his owne dūps with
thoughts. But as other beasts leuell their lookes at the
countenance of the Lion, and birdes make wing as the
Eagle flyes: so *Regis ad arbitrium totus componitur orbis:*
the people were measured by the minde of the soue-
reigne, and what stormes soeuer they smoothed in priuate conceipt, yet they made haye, and cried holiday in
outward appearance: insomuch that euerie man repaired to his owne home, and fell either vnto pleasures
or labours, as their living or content allowed them.

Whiles thus *Arcadia* rested in a silent quiet, *Menaphon* the Kings Shepheard, a man of high account
among the Swaines of *Arcadie*, loued of the Nymphes,
as the paragon of all their countrey youngsters, walking solitarie downe to the shore, to see if any of his
ewes and lambes were straggled downe to the strond to
brouse on sea iuie, wherfore they take speciall delight
to feede; he found his flockes grazing vpon the Promontorie Mountaines hardlie: whereon resting himselfe on a hill that ouer-peered the great *Mediterraneum*,
noting how *Phœbus* fetched his *Laualtos* on the purple
Plaines of *Neptunus*, as if he had meant to haue courted
Thetis in the royaltie of his roabes: the Dolphines (the
sweete conceipters of Musicke) fetcht their carreers on
the calmed waues, as if *Arion* had touched the stringes
of his siluer sounding instrument: the Mermaides

thrusting their heades from the bosome of *Amphitrite*, sate on the mounting bankes of *Neptune*, drying their waterie tresses in the Sunne beames. *Æolus* forbare to throwe abroad his gustes on the slumbering browes of the Sea-God, as giuing *Triton* leaue to pleasure his Queene with desired melodie, and *Proteus* libertie to followe his flockes without disquiet.

Menaphon looking ouer the champion of *Arcadie* to see if the Continent were as full of smiles, as the seas were of fauours, sawe the shrubbes as in a dreame with delightfull harmonie, and the birdes that chaunted on their braunches not disturbed with the least breath of a fauourable *Zephirus*. Seeing thus the accord of the Land and Sea, casting a fresh gaze on the water Nimphs, he began to consider how *Venus* was feigned by the Poets to spring of the froathe of the Seas; which draue him straight into a deepe coniecture of the inconstancie of Loue: that as if *Luna* were his load-starre, had euerie minute ebbes and tides, sometime ouerflowing the banks of Fortune with a gracious look lightened from the eyes of a fauorable louer, otherwhiles ebbing to the dangerous shelfe of despaire, with the piercing frowne of a froward Mistresse. *Menaphon* in this browne studie, calling to minde certaine Aphorismes that *Anacreon* had pend downe as principles of loues follies, being as deepe an enemie to fancie, as *Narcissus* was to affection, began thus to scoffe at *Venus* Deitie.

Menaphon thy mindes fauours, are greater than thy wealths fortunes, thy thoughtes higher than thy birth, and thy priuate conceipt better than thy publique esteeme. Thou art a shepheard *Menaphon*, who in feeding of thy flockes findest out natures secrecie, and in preuenting thy lambes preiudice conceiptest the Astronom-

icall motions of the heauens: holding thy sheep-walkes
to yeeld as great Philosophie, as the Ancients discourse
in their learned Academies. Thou countest labour as
the *Indians* doo their *Chrisocolla* wherwith they trie
euerie mettall, and thou examine euerie action. Content
sitteth in thy minde as *Neptune* in his Sea-throne, who
with his trident mace appeaseth euerie storme. When
thou seest the heauens frowne thou thinkest on thy
faults, and a cleere skie putteth thee in minde of grace:
the summers glorie tels thee of youths vanitie, the winters parched leaues of ages declining weaknes. Thus in
a myrour thou measurest thy deedes with equall and
considerate motions, and by being a shepheard findest
that which Kings wāt in their royalties. Enuie ouer-
looketh thee, renting with the windes the Pine trees of
Ida, when the *Affrick* shrubs waue not a leafe with the
tempestes. Thine eyes are vaylde with content that thou
canst not gaze so high as ambition: and for loue, and
with that in naming of loue, the shepheard fell into a
great laughter. Loue *Menaphon*, why of all follies that
euer Poets fained, or men euer faulted with, this foolish
imagination of loue is the greatest: *Venus* forsooth for
her wanton escapes must be a Goddesse, and her bastard a Deitie: *Cupide* must be yong and euer a boy to
prooue that loue is fond and witlesse, wings to make
him inconstant, and arrowes whereby to shew him feare-
ful: blinde (or all were not worth a pinne) to prooue
that *Cupides* leuell is both without aime and reason:
thus is the God, and such are his Votaries. As soone as
our shepheards of *Arcadie* settle themselues to fancie,
and weare the characters of *Venus* stampte in their for-
heads, straight their attire must bee quaint, their lookes
full of amours, as their Gods quiuer is full of arrowes;

their eyes holding smiles and teares, to leape out at their Mistres fauours or her frownes: sighes must flie as figures of their thoughts, and euerie wrinckle must be tempred with a passion: thus suted in outward proportion, and made excellent in inward constitution, they straight repaire to take viewe of their Mistres beautie. She as one obseruant vnto *Venus* principles, first tieth loue in her tresses, and wraps affection in the tramels of her haire; snaring our swains in her locks as *Mars* in the net, holding in her forhead Fortunes Calender, either to assigne dismal influence, or some fauourable aspect. If a wrinckle appeare in her brow, then our shepheard must put on his working day face, and frame nought but dolefull Madrigalls of sorrowe; if a dimple grace her cheeke, the heauens cannot prooue fatal to our kinde hearted louers; if she seeme coy, then poemes of death mounted vppon deepe drawne sighes, flie from their master to sue for some fauour, alledging how death at the least may date his miserie: to be briefe, as vppon the shoares of *Lapanthe* the winds continue neuer one day in one quarter, so the thoughtes of a louer neuer continue scarce a minute in one passion; but as Fortunes globe, so is fancies seate variable and inconstant. If louers sorrowes then be like *Sisiphus* turmoyles, and their fauours like honnie bought with gall; let poore *Menaphon* then liue at labour, and make esteeme of *Venus* as of *Mars* his concubine; and as the *Cimbrians* hold their idols in account but in euerie tempest, so make *Cupide* a God, but whẽ thou art ouerpained with passions, and that *Menaphon* wil neuer loue, for as long as thou temperest thy handes with labours, thou canst not fetter thy thoughts with loues. And in this Satyricall humor smiling at his owne con-

ceipts, hee tooke his pipe in his hand, and betweene
euerie report of his instrument sung a *stanzo* to this
effect.

Menaphons Song.

Some say Loue
Foolish Loue
   Doth rule and gouerne all the Gods,
I say Loue,
Inconstant Loue
   Sets mens senses farre at ods.
Some sweare Loue
Smooth'd face Loue
   Is sweetest sweete that men can haue:
I say Loue,
Sower Loue
   Makes vertue yeeld as beauties slaue.
A bitter sweete, a follie worst of all
That forceth wisedome to be follies thrall.
   Loue is sweete.
   Wherein sweete?
     In fading pleasures that doo paine.
   Beautie sweete.
   Is that sweete
     That yeeldeth sorrow for a gaine?
   If Loues sweete,
   Heerein sweete
     That minutes ioyes are monthlie woes.
   Tis not sweete,
   That is sweete
     Nowhere, but where repentance growes.
Then loue who list if beautie be so sower:
Labour for me, Loue rest in Princes bower.

Menaphon hauing ended his roundelay, rising vp, thinking to passe from the mountaine downe to the valley, casting his eye to the sea side, espied certain fragments of a broken ship floating vpon the waues, and sundrie persons driuen vpon the shore with a calme, walking all wet and weary vpon the sands, wondring at this strange sight he stood amazed; yet desirous to see the euent of this accident, he shrowded himself to rest vnespied til he might perceiue what would happen: at last he might descrie it was a woman holding a childe in her armes, and an olde man directing her as it were her guide. These three (as distressed wrackes) preserued by some further forepoynting fate, coueted to clime the moūtaine, the better to vse the fauor of the Sunne, to drie their drenched apparaile; at last crawled vp where poore *Menaphon* lay close, and resting them vnder a bush, the old man did nothing but sende out sighes, and the woman ceased not from streaming foorth riuolets of teares, that hung on her cheekes like the droppes of pearled deaw vppon the riches of *Flora*. The poore babe was the touch-stone of his mothers passions; for when he smiled and lay laughing in hir lappe, were her heart neuer so deeply ouercharged with her present sorrowes; yet kissing the pretie infant, shee lightened out smiles from those cheekes, that were furrowed with continual sources of teares: but if he cried, then sighes as smokes, and sobbes as thundercracks, foreranne those showers, that with redoubled distresse distilled from her eyes: thus with pretie inconstant passions trimming vp her babie, and at last to lull him a sleepe, she warbled out of her wofull breast this dittie.

Sepheſtias song to her childe.

Weepe not my wanton smile vpon my knee,
When thou art olde ther's griefe inough for thee.
 Mothers wagge, pretie boy,
 Fathers sorrow, fathers ioy;
 When thy father firſt did see
 Such a boy by him and mee,
 He was glad, I was woe,
 Fortune changde made him so,
 When he left his pretie boy,
 Laſt his sorowe, firſt his ioy.
Weepe not my wanton smile vpon my knee:
When thou art olde ther's griefe inough for thee.
 Streaming teares that neuer ſtint,
 Like pearle drops from a flint,
 Fell by course from his eyes,
 That one anothers place supplies:
 Thus he grieud in euerie part,
 Teares of bloud fell from his hart,
 When he left his pretie boy,
 Fathers sorrow, fathers ioy.
Weepe not my wanton smile vpon my knee:
When thou art olde ther's griefe inough for thee.
 The wanton smilde, father wept;
 Mother cride, babie lept:
 More he crowde, more we cride;
 Nature could not sorowe hide.
 He muſt goe, he muſt kisse
 Childe and mother, babie blisse:
 For he left his pretie boy,
 Fathers sorowe, fathers ioy.
Weepe not my wanton smile vpon my knee:
When thou art olde ther's griefe inough for thee.

With this lullaby the babie fell a sleepe, and *Sepheſtia* laying it vpon the greene grasse couered it with a mantle, and then leaning her head on her hand, and her elbow on her lap she fell a fresh to poure foorth abundaunce of plaintes, which *Lamedon* the old man espying, although in his face appeared the mappe of discontent, and in euerie wrinckle was a catalogue of woes, yet to cheere vp *Sepheſtia*, shrowding his inward sorrow with an outward smile, he began to comfort her in this manner.

Sepheſtia, thou seeſt no Phisick preuailes againſt the gaze of the Basiliſckes, no charme againſt the ſting of the *Tarantula*, no preuention to diuert the decree of the Fates, nor no meanes to recall backe the balefull hurt of Fortune: Incurable sores are without *Auicens* Aphorismes, and therefore no salue for them but patience. Then my *Sepheſtia* sith thy fal is high, and fortune low; thy sorrowes great, and thy hope little: seeing me partaker of thy miseries, set all thy reſt vppon this, *Solamen miseris, socios habuisse doloris*. Chaunce is like *Ianus* double faced, as well full of smiles to comfort, as of frownes to dismay: the Ocean at his deadeſt ebbe returns to a full tide; when the Eagle meanes to soare higheſt, hee raiseth his flight in the loweſt dales: so fareth it with fortune who in her higheſt extreames is moſt vnconſtant: when the tempeſt of her wrath is moſt fearfull, then looke for a calme; when she beates thee with nettle, then thinke she will ſtrewe thee with roses; when shee is moſt familiar with furies, her intent is to be moſt prodigall *Sepheſtia*. Thus are the arrowes of Fortune feathered with the plumes of the bird *Halcione*, that changeth colours with the Moone, which howsoeuer she shootes them pierce not so deepe but they may

bee cured. But *Sepheſtia* thou art daughter to a King,
exiled by him from the hope of a crowne, banisht from
the pleasures of the Court to the painfull fortunes of the
countrey, parted for loue from him thou canſt not but
loue, from *Maximus Sepheſtia*, who for thee hath suffered so many disfauours, as either discontent or death
can affoord. What of all this, is not hope the daughter
of time? Haue not ſtarres their fauourable aspects, as
they haue froward opposition? Is there not a *Iupiter* as
there is a *Saturne*? Cannot the influence of smiling *Venus*, ſtretch as farre as the frowning conſtitution of
Mars? I tell thee *Sepheſtia*, *Iuno* foldeth in her brows the
volumes of the Deſtinies; whom melancholie *Saturne*
deposeth from a Crowne, she mildlie aduanceth to a
Diadem: then feare not, for if the mother liue in miserie,
yet hath she a scepter for the sonne: let the vnkindnesse
of thy father be buried in the cinders of obedience, and
the want of *Maximus* be supplied with the presence of
his pretie babe, who beeing too young for Fortune, lies
smiling on thy knee and laughs at Fortune: learne by
him *Sepheſtia* to vse patience, which is like the balme in
the Vale of *Iehosaphat*, that findeth no wound so deepe,
but it cureth: thou seeſt alreadie Fortune begins to
change her view, for after the great ſtorme that rent our
shippe, we found a calme that brought vs safe to shore;
the mercie of *Neptune* was more than the enuie of
Æolus, and the discurtesie of thy father is proportioned
with the fauour of the Gods. Thus *Sepheſtia* being co-
partner of thy miserie, yet do I seeke to allay thy martyrdome: beeing sicke to my selfe, yet do I play the
Phisition to thee, wishing thou maiſt beare thy sorrowes
with as much content, as I brooke my misfortunes with
patience. As hee was readie to goe forwarde with his

perswasiue argument, *Sephestia* fetching a deepe sigh, filling her tender eyes with teares, made this replie.

Sweete *Lamedon*, once partner of my royalties, now partaker of my wants, as constant in his extreame distresse, as faithfull in higher fortunes: the Turtle pearketh not on barren trees, Doues delight not in foule cottages, the Lyon frequents no putrified haunts, friends followe not after pouertie, nor hath sinister chance anie drugges from the Phisitians, *Nullus ad amissas ibit amicus opes:* and yet *Lamedon* the misfortune of *Sephestia* abridgeth not our olde contracted amitie, thou temperest her exyle with thy banishment, and she sayling to *Styx*, thou ferriest ouer to *Phlegeton*: then *Lamedon*, saying as *Andromache* sayd to *Hector Tu Dominus, tu vir, tu mihi frater eris.* Thy aged yeres shalbe the calender of my fortunes, and thy gray haires the Paralells of mine actions. If *Lamedon* perswade *Sephestia* to content, *Portia* shall not exceede *Sephestia* in patience; if he will her to keepe a low sayle, she will vayle al her sheete; if to forget her loues, shee will quench them with labours; if to accuse *Venus* as a foe, I wil hate *Cupide* as an enemie: and seeing the Destinies haue driuen thee from a crowne, I will rest satisfied with the Countrey, placing all my delights in honouring thee, and nursing vp my pretie wanton. I will imagine a small cotage to a spacious pallaice, and thinke as great quiet in a russet coate, as in royall habilliments: *Sephestia Lamedon* will not scorne with *Iuno* to turne hir self into the shape of *Semeles* nurse, but vnknowne rest carelesse of my fortunes: the hope of times returne shal be the ende of my thoughts, the smiles of my sonne shall bee the nourishment of my hart, and the course of his youth shall be the comfort of my yeres; euerie laughter that leapes from

is lookes, shall be the holiday of my conceiptes, and
uerie teare, shal furnish out my greeues, and his
athers funerals. I haue heard them say *Lamedon*, that
ae lowest shrubbes feele the least tempests, that in the
alleis of *Affrica* is heard no thunder, that in countrey
oomes is greatest rest, and in little wealth the least dis-
uiet: dignitie treadeth vpon glasse, and honour is like
o the hearbe *Synara*, that when it bloometh most gor-
eous, then it blasteth: *Aulica vita splendida miseria*,
ourts haue golden dreames, but cotages sweet slum-
res: then *Lamedon* will I disguise my self, with my
oathes I will change my thoughts; for being poorelie
tired I will be meanelie minded, and measure my ac-
ons by my present estate, not by former fortunes. In
ying this the babe awakte and cride, and she fell to
ares mixed with a lullabie.

All this while *Menaphon* sate amongst the shrubs fix-
g his eyes on the glorious obiect of her face, hee noted
er tresses, which hee compared to the coloured *Hia-
ath* of *Arcadia*, her browes to the mountaine snowes
at lie on the hils, her eyes to the gray glister of *Titans*
rgeous mantle, her alabaster necke to the whitenesse
his flockes, her teares to pearle, her face to borders of
llies interseamed with Roses: to be briefe our shep-
ard *Menaphon* that heeretofore was an Atheist to loue,
d as the *Thessalian* of *Bacchus*, so hee a contemner of
nus, was nowe by the wylie shaft of *Cupid* so intan-
ed in the perfection and beauteous excellence of *Se-
estia*; as now he swore no beningne Planet but *Venus*,
God but *Cupide*, no exquisite deitie but Loue. Being
us fettered with the pliant perswasions of fancie, im-
ient in his newe affections, as the horse that neuer
ore felt the spurre, he could not bridle his new cõ-

D

ceaued amors, but watching when they shoulde depart
perceiuing by the gestures of the olde man, and the
teares of the Gentlewoman, that they were distrest
thought to offer anie helpe that laie within the compasse
of his abilitie. As thus he mused in his new passions
Lamedon and *Sephestia* rose vp, and resolued to take
their course which way the winde blew: passing so
downe the mountaine to goe seeke out some towne, a
last they pacing softlie on, *Lamedon* espied *Menaphon*
desirous therefore to know the course of the countrey
hee saluted him thus.

Shepheard, for so farre thy attire warrants me; cour
teous, for so much thy countenance imports: if distres
sed persons whom Fortune hath wronged, and the sea
haue fauored, (if we may count it fauour to liue an
want) may without offence craue so farre ayde as t
know some place where to rest our wearie and weather
beaten bones, our charges shall be paid, and you hau
for recompence such thankes as Fortunes outlawes ma
yeeld to their fauourers. *Menaphon* hearing him spea
so grauelie, but not fitting his eare to his eye, stoo
staring still on *Sephestias* face, which shee perceiuing
flashed out such a blush frõ her alablaster cheeks tha
they lookt like the ruddie gates of the Morning: th
sweete bashfulnesse amazing *Menaphon*, at last hee b
gan thus to answere.

Strangers, your degree I know not, therefore pardo
if I giue lesse title thã your estates merit: Fortune
frownes are Princes fortunes, and Kings are subiect
chance and destinie. Mishap is to be salued with piti
not scorne: and we that are Fortunes darlings, a
bounde to relieue them that are distrest: therefore fo
low me, and you shal haue such succour, as a shephea

may affoord. *Lamedon* and *Sephestia* were passing glad,
and *Menaphon* led the way, not content onelie to feed
his sight with the beautie of his new Mistres, but
thought also to inferre some occasion of parley, to heare
whether her voyce were as melodious, as her face beautiful, hee therefore prosecuted his prattle thus. Gentlewoman, when first I saw you sitting vpon the *Arcadian*
Promontorie with your babie on your lappe, and this
olde father by; I thought I had seene *Venus* with *Cupide*
on her knee courted by *Anchises* of *Troy*: the excellence
of your looks could discouer no lesse than *Mars* his
paramour, and the beautie of the childe as much as the
dignitie of her wanton: at last perceiuing by your teares
and your childs shrikes, that ye were passengers distrest,
I lent you sighes to partake your sorrowes, and luke
warme drops to signifie how I pitie ouercharged persons, in lieu whereof let mee craue your name, countrey,
and parentage. *Sephestia* seeing by the shepheards passionate lookes, that the swaine was halfe in loue, replyed
thus; Curteous shepheard, if my blubbered cheekes did
look like *Venus* at a blush, it was when the wofull Goddesse wept for her faire *Adonis*, my boye is no *Cupide*
but the sonne of care, Fortunes fondling in his youth,
to bee I hope her darling in his age: in that your lookes
saw our griefe, and your thoughts pitied our woes, our
tõgues shal giue thanks (the bountie of sorrowes ten-
ants) and our hearts praye that the Gods may be as
friendly to your flockes, as you fauourable to vs. My
name is *Samela*, my countrey *Cipres*, my parentage
meane, the wife of a poore Gentleman nowe deceased:
how we arriued heere by shipwrack, gentle shepheard
inquire not, least it be tedious for thee to heare it, and a
double griefe for mee to rehearse it. The shepheard not

daring displease his Miſtres, as hauing loues threates
hanging on her lippes, he conueighed them home to his
house: as soone as they were arriued there, he began at
the dore to entertain them thus. Faire Miſtres the flower of all our Nymphes that liue heere in *Arcadia*, this is
my cotage wherein I liue content, and your lodging,
where (please it you) ye may reſt quiet. I haue not rich
cloathes of *Ægypt* to couer the walls, nor ſtore of place
to discouer anie wealth; for shepheards vse neither to be
proud nor couetous: you shall find heere cheese and
milke for dainties, and wooll for cloathing; in euerie
corner of the house Content sitting smiling, and tem-
pering euerie homelie thing with a welcome: this if ye
can brooke and accept of, (as Gods allow the meaneſt
hospitalitie) ye shall haue such welcome and fare as
Philemon and *Baucis* gaue to *Iupiter*. *Sepheſtia* thankt
him heartelie, and going into his house found what he
promiſt: after that they had sate a little by the fire and
were well warmed, they went to supper, where *Sepheſtia*
fedde well, as one whom the sea had made hungrie, and
Lamedon so plide his teeth, that all supper he spake not
one word: after they had taken their repaſt, *Menaphon*
seeing they were wearie, and that sleepe chimed on to
reſt, he let them see their lodging, and so gaue them the
good night. *Lamedon* on his flocke bedde, and *Sepheſtia*
on her countrey couch were so wearie, that they slept
well: but *Menaphon*, poore *Menaphon* neither asked his
swaynes for his sheepe, nor tooke his mole-spade on his
necke to see his paſtures; but as a man pained with a
thousand passions, drenched in diſtresse, and ouer-
whelmed with a multitude of vncouth cares, he sate like
the pictures that *Perseus* tourned with his *Gorgons* head
into ſtones. His siſter *Carmela* kept his house, (for so

was the Countrey wench called) and shee seeing her
brother sit so malcontented, stept to her cupboorde and
fetcht a little beaten spice in an olde bladder, she sparde
no euening milke, but went amongst the cream bowles,
and made him a posset. But alas, Loue had so lockt vp
the shepheards stomacke, that none would down with
Menaphon: *Carmela* seeing her brother refuse his spicte
drinke, thought all was not well, and therefore sate
downe and wept; to be short, she blubbered and he
sightht, and his men that came in and sawe their master
with a kercher on his head mournde; so that amongst
these swaines there was such melodie, that *Menaphon*
tooke his bow and arrowes and went to bedde: where
casting himselfe, he thought to haue beguiled his passions with some sweete slumbers. But Loue that smiled
at his newe interteined champion, sitting on his beddes
head, prickt him forward with new desires; charging
Morpheus, *Phobetor*, and *Icolon* the Gods of sleepe, to
present vnto his closed eies the singular beautie and
rare perfections of *Samela*: (for so will we now call her)
in that the *Idea* of her excellence, forst him to breath out
scalding sighes smothered within the fornace of his
thoughts, which grew into this or the like passion.

I had thought *Menaphon*, that he which weareth the
bay leafe had been free from lightening, and the Eagles
penne a preseruatiue against thunder; that labour had
been enemie to loue, and the eschewing of idlenesse an
Antidote against fancie: but I see by proofe there is no
adamant so harde, but the blood of a Goate will make
soft; no fort so wel defenced, but strong batterie will
enter; nor anie hart so pliant to restlesse labours, but
inchantments of loue will ouercome. Vnfortunate *Men-*
aphon, that a late thoughtst *Venus* a strumpet and her

sonne a bastard, now must thou offer incense at her
shrine, and sweare *Cupide* no lesse than a God : thou
hast reason *Menaphon*; for hee that liues without loue,
liues without life; presuming as *Narcissus* to hate all,
and beeing like him at length despised of all. Can there
bee a sweeter blisse than beautie, a greater heauen than
her heauenly perfections that is mistres of thy thoughts?
If the sparkle of her eyes appeare in the night, the
starres blush at her brightnesse : if her haire glister in
the daye, *Phœbus* puts off his wreath of diamonds, as
ouercome with the shine of her tresses; if she walke in
the fields, *Flora* seeing her face, bids al her glorious
flowers close themselues, as being by her beautie disgraced; if her alabaster necke appeere, then *Hiems*
couereth his snowe, as surpassed in whitenesse. To be
shorte *Menaphon*, if *Samela* had appeared in *Ida*, *Iuno*
ror maiestie, *Pallas* for wisedome, and *Venus* for beautie
had let my *Samela* haue the supremacie : why shouldest
thou not then loue, and thinke there is no life to loue,
seeing the end of loue is the possession of such a
heauenly Paragon? But what of this *Menaphon* hast
thou anie hope to enioy her person, she is a widdow,
true, but too high for thy fortunes ; she is in distresse,
ah *Menaphon*, if thou hast anie sparke of comfort, this
must set thy hope on fire. Want is the load stone of affection, distresse forceth deeper than Fortunes frownes,
and such as are poore will rather loue than want reliefe,
fortunes frownes are whetstones to fancie : and as the
horse starteth at the spurre, so loue is prickt forward
with distresse. *Samela* is shipwrackt, *Menaphon* relieues
her; she wants, he supplies with wealth; he sues for
loue, either must she grant, or buy deniall with perpetuall repentance. In this hope rested the poore shep-

hearde, and with that *Menaphon* laide head downe the pillow and toke a sounnd nappe, sleeping out fancie, with a good slumber.

As soone as the sunne appeared the shepheard got him vp, and fed fat with this hope, went merely with his men to the foldes, and there letting foorth his sheepe, after that hee had appointed where they should graze, returned home, and looking when his guests should rise, hauing supt il the last night went roundly to his breakfast: by that time he had ended his *desiune*, *Lamedon* was gotten vp, and so was *Samela*. Against their rising *Carmela* had showen her cookerie, and *Menaphon* tired in his russet iacket, his redde sleeues of chamlet, his blew bonnet, and his round slop of countrey cloth, bestirred him, as euerie ioynt had been set to a sundrie office. *Samela* no sooner came out of her chamber, but *Menaphon* as one that claimed pitie for his passions, bad her good morrow with a firme louers looke: *Samela* knowing the fowle by the feather, was able to cast his disease without his water, perceiued that *Cupide* had caught the poore shepheard in his net, and vnles he sought quickly to break out of the snare would make him a tame foole: faire lookes she gaue him, and with a smiling sorow discouered how she grieued at his misfortune, and yet fauoured him. Well, to breakfast they went *Lamedon* and *Samela* fed hard, but *Menaphon* like the *Argiue* in the Date gardens of *Arabia*, liued with the contemplation of his Mistres beautie: the Salamander liueth not without the fire, the Herring from the water, the Mole from the earth, nor the Cameleon from the aire, nor coulde *Menaphon* liue from the sight of his *Samela*; whose breath was perfumed aire, whose eyes were fire wherein he delighted to dallie, whose heart the earthlie Paradice wherein hee desired to ingraffe the essence of his loue and affection: thus did the poore shepheard bathe in a kinde of blisse, whiles his eye feeding on his mistres face, did surfet with the excellencie of her perfection. So long he gazde, that at length breakfast was ended, and he desirous to doo her anie seruice, first put her childe to nurse, and then led her forth to see his folds; thinking with the sight of his flockes to inueigle her, whose minde had rather haue chosen anie misfortune, than haue deined her eyes on the face and feature of so lowe a peasant. Well, abroad they went, *Menaphon* with his sheephooke fringed with cruell, to signifie he was chiefe of the swaynes, *Lamedon* and *Samela* after: plodding thus ouer the greene fields, at last they came to the mountains where *Menaphōs* flockes grazed, and there he discoursed vnto *Samela* thus; I tell thee faire Nymph, these Plaines that thou seest stretching Southward, are pastures belonging to *Menaphon*: there growes the cintfoyle, and the hyacinth, the cowsloppe, the primrose, and the violet, which my flockes shall spare for flowers to make thee garlands, the milke of my ewes shall be meate for thy pretie wanton, the wool of the fat weathers that seemes as fine as the fleece that *Iason* fet from *Colchos*, shall serue to make *Samela* webbes withall; the mountaine tops shall be thy mornings walke, and the shadie valleies thy euenings arbour: as much as *Menaphon* owes shall be at *Samelas* command, if she like to liue with *Menaphon*. This was spoken with such deepe effects, that *Samela* could scarce keepe her from smiling, yet she couered her conceipt with a sorrowful countenance, which *Menaphon* espying, to make her merrie, and rather for his own aduantage, seeing *Lamedon* was a sleepe, tooke her

by the hand and sate downe, and pulling foorth his pipe,
began after some melodie to caroll out this roundelay.

Menaphons roundelay.

When tender ewes brought home with euening Sunne
Wend to their foldes,
And to their holdes
The shepheards trugde when light of day is done.
Vpon a tree
The Eagle Ioues *faire bird did pearch,*
There resteth hee.
A little flie his harbor then did search,
And did presume (though others laught thereat)
To pearch where as the princelie Eagle sat.

The Eagle frownd, and shooke her royall wings;
And chargde the Flie
From thence to hie:
Afraid in hast the little creature flings,
Yet seekes againe
Fearfull to pearke him by the Eagles side.
With moodie vaine
The speedie post of Ganimede *replide;*
Vassaile auant or with my wings you die,
Ist fit an Eagle seate him with a Flie?

The Flie craude pitie, still the Eagle frownde,
The sillie Flie
Readie to die
Disgracte, displacte, fell groueling to the ground.

The Eagle sawe
And with a royall minde said to the Flie,
Be not in awe,
I scorne by me the meanest creature die;
Then seate thee heere: the ioyfull Flie vp flings,
And sate safe shadowed with the Eagles wings.

As soone as *Menaphon* had ended this roundelay, turning to *Samela*, after a countrey blush, he began to court her in this homely fashion; What thinke you *Samela* of the Eagle for this royall deede? That he falsified the olde Prouerbe *Aquila non capit muscas*. But I meane *Samela* are you not in opinion, that the Eagle giues instance of a princelie resolution, in preferring the safetie of a Flie before the credit of her royall Maiestie? I thinke *Menaphon* that high minds are the shelters of pouertie, and Kings seates are couerts for distressed persons; that the Eagle in shrowding the Flie did well, but a little forgot her honour. But how thinke you *Samela*, is not this proportion to be obserued in loue? I gesse no, for the Flie did it not for loue, but for succour. Hath loue then respect of circumstance? Els it is not loue, but lust; for where the parties haue no simpathie of Estates, there can no firme loue be fixed; discord is reputed the mother of diuision, and in nature this is an vnrefuted principle, that it falteth which faileth in vniformitie. He that grafteth Iillyflowers vpon the Nettle marreth the smell; who coueteth to tie the Lambe and the Lion in one tedder maketh a brawle; equall fortunes are loues fauourites, and therefore shoulde fancie bee always limitted by Geometricall proportion; least if young matching with olde, fire and frost fall at a combate: and if rich with poore there happe manie daungerous and brauing obiections. *Menaphon* halfe nipte in the pate with this replie, yet like at all souldier stoode to his tackling, and made this aunswere; Suppose gentle *Samela*, that a man of meane estate, whome disdainefull Fortune had abased, intending to make hir power prodigall in his misfortunes, being feathered with *Cupides* bolt, were snared in the beautie of a Queene, should he rather die than discouer his amors? If Queens (quoth she) were of my mind, I had rather die, thã perish in baser fortunes. *Venus* loued *Vulcan* replied *Menaphon*: truth quoth *Samela*, but though he was polt-footed, yet he was a God. *Phaon* enioyed *Sapho* he a Ferriman that liued by his hands thrift, she a Princesse that fate inuested with a diadem. The more fortunate quoth *Samela* was he in his honours, and she the lesse famous in her honestie. To leaue these instances replied *Menaphon*, (for loue had made him hardie) I sweete *Samela* inferre these presupposed premisses, to discouer the basenesse of my mean birth, and yet the deepnesse of my affection, who euer since I saw the brightnesse of your perfection shining vpon the moũtains of *Arcadie*, like the glister of the Sunne vpon the toplesse Promontorie of *Sicilia*, was so snared with your beautie, and so inueigled with the excellẽce of that perfection that exceedeth all excellencie, that loue entring my desire, hath mainteined himselfe by force; that vnlesse sweete *Samela* grant me fauour of her loue, and play the princelie Eagle, I shall with the poore Flie perish in my Fortunes: he concluded this period with a deepe sigh, and *Samela* grieuing at this follie of the Shephearde, gaue him mildelie this aunswere.

Menaphon my distressed haps are the resolutions of the Destinies, and the wrongs of my youth, are the fore-

runners of my woes in age; my natiue home is my worst
nurserie, and my friends denie that which strangers
preiudiciallie grant: I arriued in *Arcady* shipwrackt, and
Menaphon fauouring my sorrowes hath affoorded me
succours, for which *Samela* rests bound, and will prooue
thankfull: as for loue, knowe that *Venus* standeth on the
Tortoys, as shewing that Loue creepeth on by degrees;
that affection is like the Snayle, which stealeth to the
top of the lance by minutes: the grasse hath his increase,
yet neuer anie sees it augment, the Sonne shadowes,
but the motion is not seene; loue like those should enter
into the eye, and by long gradations passe into the
heart; *Cupid* hath wings to flie, not that loue should be
swift, but that he may soare high to auoyd base thoughts.
The Topace being throwne into the fire burneth
straight, but no sooner out of the flame but it freezeth;
strawe is soone kindled, but it is but a blaze; and loue
that is caught in a moment, is lost in a minute: giue me
leaue then *Menaphon* first to sorrow for my fortunes,
then to call to minde my husbands late funeralls, then if
the Fates haue assigned I shall fancie, I will account of
thee before anie shepheard in *Arcadie*. This conclusion
of *Samela* draue *Menaphon* into such an extasie for ioy,
that he stood as a man metamorphozed; at last calling
his senses together, hee tolde her he rested satisfied with
her answere, and therupon lent her a kisse, such as
blushing *Thetis* receaues from her choycest lemman. At
this *Lamedon* awakte, otherwise *Menaphon* no doubt
had replied, but breaking off their talk they went to
view their pastures, and so passing downe to the place
where the sheepe grazed, they searched the shepheards
bagges, and so emptied their bottles as *Samela* mer-
uailed at such an vncouth banquet: at last they returned

ome, *Menaphon* glorying in the hope of his successe,
nterteining *Samela* still with such courtesie, that shee
inding such cõtent in the cotage, began to despise the
onors of the Court. Resting thus in house with the
hepheard, to auoide tedious conceipts she framed her
elfe so to countrey labours, that she oft times would
ead the flocks to the fieldes her selfe, and being drest in
omelie attire, she seemd like *Oenone* that was amorous
f *Paris*. As she thus often traced alongst the Plaines,
he was noted amongst the shepheardes of one *Doron*
ext neighbour to *Menaphon*, who entered into the con-
ideration of her beautie, and made report of it to all
is fellow swaines, so that they chatted nought in the
ields but of the new shepheardesse. One daye amongst
he rest, it chaunced that *Doron* sitting in parley with
nother countrey companion of his, amidst other tattle,
hey prattled of the beautie of *Samela*. Hast thou seene
er quoth *Melicertus*, (for so was his friend called) I
uoth *Doron* and sigtht to see her, not that I was in
oue, but that I greeued shee shuld be in loue with such
one as *Menaphon*. What mauner of woman is shee
uoth *Melicertus*? As well as I can answered *Doron* I will
nake description of her.

Dorons description of *Samela*.

Like to Diana *in her Summer weede*
Girt with a crimson roabe of brightest die,
                    goes faire Samela.
Whiter than be the flockes that straggling feede,
When washt by Arethusa *faint they lie:*
                    is faire Samela.

As faire Aurora *in her morning gray*
Deckt with the ruddie glister of her loue,
                    is faire Samela.
Like louelie Thetis *on a calmed day,*
When as her brightnesse Neptunes *fancie moue,*
                    shines faire Samela.
Her tresses gold, her eyes like glassie streames,
Her teeth are pearle, the breasts are yuorie
                    of faire Samela.
Her cheekes like rose and lilly yeeld foorth gleames,
Her browes bright arches framde of ebonie:
                    Thus faire Samela.
Passeth faire Venus *in her brauest hiew,*
And Iuno *in the shew of maiestie,*
                    for she'is Samela.
Pallas *in wit, all three if you well view,*
For beautie, wit, and matchlesse dignitie
                    yeeld to Samela.

Thou hast quoth *Melicertus* made such a description,
as if *Priamus* young boy should paint out the perfection
of his Greekish Paramour. Me thinkes the *Idea* of her
person represents it selfe an obiect to my fantasie, and
that I see in the discouerie of her excellence, the rare
beauties of: and with that he broke off abruptlie with
such a deepe sigh, as it seemed his heart should haue
broken; sitting as the *Lapithes* when they gazed on
Medusa. *Doron* meruailing at this sodayne euent, was
halfe afraid, as if some appoplexie had astonied his
senses, so that cheering vp his friend, he demanded
what the cause was of this sodaine conceipt. *Melicertus*
no niggarde in discouerie of his fortunes, began thus. I
tell thee *Doron* before I kept sheepe in *Arcadie*, I was

a Shepheard else where, so famous for my flockes, as *Menaphon* for his foldes; beloued of the Nymphes, as hee likte of the Countrey Damzells; coueting in my loues to vse *Cupids* wings, to soare high in my desires, though my selfe were borne to base fortunes. The Hobbie catcheth no pray, vnlesse she mount beyonde her marke, the Palme tree beareth most bowes where it groweth highest, and Loue is most fortunate where his courage is resolute, and thought beyond his compasse. Grounding therefore on these principles, I fixte mine eye on a Nymph, whose parentage was great, but her beautie farre more excellent, her birth was by manie degrees greater than mine, and my woorth by manie discents lesse than hers: yet knowing *Venus* loued *Adonis*, and *Luna Endymion*, that *Cupide* had boltes feathered with the plumes of a Crowe, as well as with the pennes of an Eagle, I attempted and courted her, I found her lookes lightening disdaine, and her forhead to conteine fauours for others, and frownes for me: when I alledged faith, she crost me with *Æneas*, when loyaltie, she tolde me of *Iason*; whẽ I swore constancie, shee questioned me of *Demophoon*; when I craued a finall resolution to my fatall passions, shee filde her browes full of wrinckles, and her eyes full of furie, turned her backe, and shooke me off with a *Non placet*. Thus in loues I lost loues, and for her loue had lost all, had not when I neere despaired the clemencie of some curteous starre, or rather the verie excellence of my Mistres fauours salued my halfe despairing maladie: for shee seeing that I helde a supersticious opinion of loue, in honouring him for a Deitie, not in counting him a vaine conceipt of Poetrie, that I thought it sacriledge to wrong my desires, and the basest fortune to inhance my fortune by falsing my loues to a woman, she left from being so rammage, and gentlie came to the fiſt, and granted me those fauours shee might affoord, or my thoughts desire: with this he ceaſt and fell againe to his sighes, which *Doron* noting, answered thus. If (my good *Melicertus*) thou didſt enioy thy loues, what is the occasion thou beginneſt with sighes, and endeſt with passions. Ah *Doron* there endes my ioyes, for no sooner had I triumpht in my fauours, but the trophees of my fortunes fell like the hearbes in *Syria*, that flourish in the morne, and fade before night; or like vnto the flie *Tyryma*, that taketh life and leaueth it all in one day. So my *Doron* did it fare with me, for I had no sooner enioyed my loue, but the heauens enuious a shepheard should haue the fruition of such a heauenly Paragon, sent vnreuocable Fates to depriue me of her life, and shee is dead: dead *Doron*, to her, to my selfe, to all, but not to my memorie, for so deepe were the characters ſtamped in my inwarde senses, that obliuion can neuer race out the forme of her excellence. And with that he ſtart vp, seeking to fall out of those dumpes with Musique, (for he plaid on his pipe certaine sonets he had contriued in praise of the countrey wenches) but plaine *Doron* as plaine as a packſtaffe, desired him to sound a roundelay, and he would sing a song, which he carolled to this effect.

Dorons Iigge.

Through the shrubbes as I can cracke,
        For my Lambes little ones,
        Mongſt many pretie ones,
Nimphes I meane, whose haire was blacke
                        As the crow:
                        Like the snow

Her face and browes shinde I weene:
    I saw a little one,
    A bonny prety one,
As bright, buxsome and as sheene
            As was shee,
            On hir knee
That lulld the God, whose arrowes warmes
    Such merry little ones,
    Such faire fac'd prety ones,
As dally in Loues chiefest harmes,
            Such was mine:
            Whose gray eyne

Made me loue. I gan to woo
    This sweete little one,
    This bonny pretie one.
I wooed hard a day or two,
            Till she bad;
            Be not sad,

Wooe no more I am thine owne,
    Thy dearest little one,
    Thy truest pretie one:
Thus was faith and firme loue showne,
            As behoues
            Shepheards loues.

How like you this Dittie of mine owne deuising, quoth *Doron?* As well as my musique replied *Melicertus*; for if *Pan* and I striue, *Midas* being Iudge, and should happe to giue me the garland, I doubt not but his Asses eares should be doubled: but *Doron* so long we dispute of loue, and forget our labours, that both our flockes shall be vnfolded, and tomorrow our merrie meeting hindered. Thats true quoth *Doron*, for there will be all

E

the shepheards Daughters and countrey Damzels, and
amongst them feare not but *Menaphon* will bring his
faire Shepheardesse, there *Melicertus* shalt thou see her
that will amate all our moodes, and amaze thee, and
therefore good *Melicertus* let vs be going. With this
prattle away they went to their foldes, where we leaue
them, and returne to *Menaphon*, who triumphing in the
hope of his new loues, caused *Samela* to tricke her vp in
her countrey attire, and make her selfe braue against the
meeting: she that thought, to be coye were to discouer
her thoughts, drest her selfe vp in *Carmelas* russet cas-
socke, and that so quaintly, as if *Venus* in a countrey
peticoate had thought to wanton it with her louely *A-
donis*. The morow came, and away they went, but *Lamedon* was left behinde to keep the house. At the houre
appointed, *Menaphon*, *Carmela* and *Samela* came, when
all the rest were readie making merie. As soone as word
was brought, that *Menaphon* came with his newe Mistres, all the companie began to murmur, and euery man
to prepare his eye for so miraculous an obiect: but *Pesana* a heardsmans daughter of the same parish, that
long had loued *Menaphon*, and he had filled her browes
with frownes, her eyes with furie, and her heart with
griefe; yet coueting in so open an assemblie, as well as
shee coulde to hide a pad in the straw, she expected as
others did the arriuall of her newe corriuall: who at that
instant came with *Menaphon* into the house. No sooner
was she entred the Parlour, but her eyes gaue such a
shine, and her face such a brightnesse, that they stood
gazing on this Goddesse; and shee vnacquainted, seeing
her selfe among so manie vnknowen swaines, died her
cheekes with such a vermilion blush, that the countrey
maides themselues fel in loue with his faire Nimph, and

could not blame *Menaphon* for being ouer the shooes
with such a beautifull creature. *Doron* iogde *Melicertus*
on the elbowe, and so awakte him out of a dreame, for
he was deeply drownd in the contemplation of her excellencie; sending out vollies of sighs in remembrance
of his old loue, as thus hee sate meditating on her fauour, how much she resembled her that death had de-
priued him off: well her welcome was great of all the
companie, and for that she was a stranger they graced
her to make her the mistres of the Feast. *Menaphon*
seeing *Samela* thus honoured, conceiued no smal content in the aduancing of his Mistres, being passing
ioconde and pleasant with the rest of the companie, insomuch that euerie one perceiued howe the poore
swayne fedde vppon the dignities of his Mistres graces.
Pesana noting this began to lowre, and *Carmela* wink-
ing vpon her fellowes, answered her frownes with a
smile, which doubled her griefe; for womens paines are
more pinching if they be girded with a frumpe, than
if they be galled with a mischiefe. Whiles thus there
was banding of such lookes, as euerie one imported as
much as an *impreso*, *Samela* willing to see the fashion of
these countrey yong frowes, cast her eyes abroad, and
in viewing euerie face, at last her eyes glaunced on the
lookes of *Melicertus*; whose countenance resembled so
vnto her dead Lord, that as a woman astonied she stood
staring on his face, but ashamed to gaze vppon a
stranger, she made restraint of her looks, and so taking
her eye from one particular obiect, she sent it abroad to
make generall suruey of their countrey demeanours.
But amidst all this gazing, he that had seene poore
Menaphon, how infected with a iealous furie, he stared
each man in the face, fearing their eyes should feede or

surfet on his Miſtres beautie: if they glaunſt, he thought ſtraight they would be riualls in his loues; if they flatlie lookt, then they were deepely snared in affection; if they once smiled on her, they had receyued some glance from *Samela* that made them so malepart; if she laught, she likte; and at that he began to frowne: thus sate poore *Menaphon* all dinner while pained with a thousande iealous passions, keeping his teeth garders of his ſtomacke, and his eyes watchmen of his loues, but *Melicertus* halfe impatientof his new conceiued thoughts, determined to trie how the Damzell was brought vp, and whether she was as wise as beautifull, hee therefore began to breake silence thus.

The Orgies which the *Bacchanals* kept in *Thessaly*, the Feaſts which the melancholy *Saturniſts* foũded in *Danuby*, were neuer so quatted with silence, but on their feſtiual daies they did frolicke amongſt themselues with manie pleasaunt parlies: were it no a shame then that we of *Arcadie*, famous for the beautie of our Nymphes, and the amorous roundelaies of our shepheards, shoulde disgrace *Pans* holiday with such melancholy dumpes: curteous countrey Swaines shake off this sobrietie, and seeing we haue in our companie Damzels both beautifull and wise, let vs interteine them with prattle, to trie our wittes, and tire our time; to this they all agreed with a *plaudite*. Then quoth *Melicertus*; by your leaue since I was first in motion, I will be first in queſtion, and therefore new come shepheardesse firſt to you: at this *Samela* blusht, and he began thus.

Faire Damzel, when *Næreus* chatted with *Iuno*, he had pardon, in that his prattle came more to plesure the Goddesse than to ratifie his owne presumption: if I Miſtres be ouerbold, forgiue me; I queſtion not to

offend, but to set time free from tediousnesse. Then
gentle shepheardesse tell me, if you should bee transformed through the anger of the Gods, into some shape;
what creature would you reason to be in forme? *Samela*
blushing that she was the firſt that was boorded, yet
gathered vp her crums, and desirous to shew her preg-
naunt wit, (as the wiseſt women be euer tickled with
self loue) made him this answere.

Gentle shepheard, it fits not ſtrangers to be nice, nor
maidens too coy; leaſt the one feele the weight of a
scoffe, the other the fall of a frumpe: pithie queſtions
are mindes whetſtones, and by discoursing in ieſt,
manie doubts are deciphered in earneſt: therefore you
haue foreſtalled me in crauing pardon, when you haue
no neede to feele anie grant of pardon. Therefore thus to
your queſtion; *Daphne* I remember was turned to a bay
tree, *Niobe* to a flint, *Lampetia* and her siſters to flowers,
and sundrie Virgins to sundrie shapes according to
their merites; but if my wish might serue for a Metamorphosis, I would be turned into a sheepe. A sheepe,
and why so Miſtres? I reason thus quoth *Samela*, my
supposition should be simple, my life quiet, my food
the pleasant Plaines of *Arcadie* and the wealthie riches
of *Flora*, my drinke the coole ſtreames that flowe from
the concaue Promontorie of this Continent, my aire
should bee cleere, my walkes spacious, my thoughts at
ease, and can there none shepheard be my better premisses to conclude my replie than these? But haue you no
other allegations to confirme your resolution? Yes sir
quoth she, and farre greater. Then the law of our firſt
motion quoth hee commands you to repeate them.
Farre be it answered *Samela* that I should not doo of
free will anie thing that this pleasant companie com-

mands: therefore thus; Were I a sheepe, I should bee garded from the foldes with iollie Swaines, such as was *Lunas* Loue on the hills of *Latmos*; their pipes sounding like the melodie of *Mercurie*, when he lulld asleepe *Argus*: but more, when the Damzells tracing along the Plaines, should with their eyes like Sunne bright beames, drawe on lookes to gaze on such sparkling Planets: then wearie with foode, shoulde I lye and looke on their beauties, as on the spotted wealthe of the richest Firmament; I should listen to their sweete layes, more sweete than the Sea-borne *Syrens*: thus feeding on the delicacie of their features, I should like the *Tyrian* heyfer fall in loue with *Agenors* darling. I but quoth *Melicertus*, those faire facde Damzells oft draw foorth the kindest sheepe to the shambles. And what of that sir aunswered *Samela*, would not a sheepe so long fed with beautie, die for loue. If he die (quoth *Pesana*) it is more kindnes in beasts, than constancie in men: for they die for loue, when larkes die with leekes. If they be so wise quoth *Menaphon*, they shew but their mother witts; for what sparkes they haue of inconstancie, they drawe from their female fosterers, as the Sea dooth ebbes and tides from the Moone. So be it sir answered *Pesana*, then no doubt your mother was made of a Weathercocke, that brought foorth such a wauering companion: for you master *Menaphon* measure your looks by minutes and your loues are like lightning, which no sooner flash on the eie, but they vanish. It is then quoth *Menaphon* because mine eye is a foolish Iudge, and chooseth too baselie: which when my heart censures of, it casts away as refuse. Twere best thẽ said *Pesana*, to discharge such vniust Iudges of ther seates, and to set your eares hearers of your loue pleas. If they fault quoth

Melicertus, euerie market towne hath a remedie, or els
there is neuer a Baker neere by seauen miles. Stay curteous Shepheards quoth *Samela*, these iestes are too
broade before, they are cynicall like *Diogenes* quippes,
that had large feathers and sharpe heads, it little fits in
this companie to bandie taunts of loue, seeing you are
vnwedded and these all maidens addicted to chastitie.
You speake well as a Patronesse of our credite quoth
Pesana, for indeede we be virgins, and addicted to virginitie. Now quoth *Menaphon* that you haue got a virgin
in your mouth you wil neuer leaue chaunting that word,
till you prooue your selfe either a Vestall or a Sybill.
Suppose she were a Vestall quoth *Melicertus*, I had almost said a virgine (but God forbidde I had made such
a doubtfull supposition) shee might carrie water with
Amulia in a siue: for amongst all the rest of the virgins
we read of none but her that wrought such a miracle.
Pesana hearing how pleasantly *Melicertus* plaid with her
nose, thought to giue him as great a bone to gnaw
vppon, which she cast in his teeth thus briefelie.

I remember sir that *Epicurus* measured euerie mans
diet by his owne principles; *Abradas* the great *Macedonian* Pirate, thought euerie one had a letter of Marte,
that bare sayles in the Ocean; none came to knocke at
Diogenes tub but was supposed a Cinick; and fancie a
late hath so tied you to his vanities, that you will thinke
Vesta a flat figured conceipt of Poetrie. *Samela* perceiuing these blowes woulde growe to deepe wounds, broke
off their talke with this prety digression. Gentlemen, to
end this strife, I praye you let vs heare the opinion of
Doron, for all this while neither he nor *Carmela* haue
vttered one word, but sate as Censers of our pleas;
twere necessarie he tolde vs how his heart came thus on

his halfepenie. *Doron* hearing *Samela* thus pleasaunt, made presentlie this blunt replie; I was faire Mistres in a solempne doubt with my selfe, whether in beeing a sheepe, you would be a Ram or an Ewe? An Ewe no doubt quoth *Samela*, for hornes are the heauiest burden that the head can beare. As *Doron* was readie to replie, came in sodainly to this parley foure or fiue olde shep-heards, who broke off their prattle, that from that they fel to drinking: and so after some parley of their flocks, euerie one departed to their own home where they talked of the exquisite perfection of *Samela*, especially *Melicertus*, who gotten to his owne cotage, and lyen downe in his couch by himselfe, began to ruminate on *Samelas* shape.

Ah *Melicertus*, what an obiect fortune this day brought to thy eyes, presenting a strange *Idæa* to thy sight, as appeared to *Achilles* of his dead friend *Patroclus*, tresses of gold like the tramels of *Sephestias* lockes, a face fairer than *Venus*, such was *Sephestia*; her eye paints her out *Sephestia*, her voyce sounds her out *Sephestia*, she seemeth none but *Sephestia*: but seing she is dead, and there liueth not such another *Sephestia*, sue to her and loue her, for that it is either a selfe same or another *Sephestia*. In this hope *Melicertus* fel to his slumber, but *Samela* was not so content: for shee began thus to muse with her selfe; May this *Melicertus* be a shep-heard? or can a countrie cotage affoord such perfection? doth this coast bring forth such excellence? then happie are the virgins shall haue such suters, and the wiues such pleasing husbands; but his face is not inchacte with anie rusticke proportion, his browes containe the characters of nobilitie, and his lookes in shepheards weeds are Lordlie, his voyce pleasing, his wit full of

gentrie: weigh all these equallie, and consider *Samela* is
it not thy *Maximus?* Fond foole away with these suppositions; could the dreaming of *Andromache* call *Hector*
from his graue? or can the vision of my husband raise
him from the seas? Tush stoop not to such vanities: hee
is dead, and therefore grieue not thy memorie with the
imagination of his new reuiue, for there hath been but
one *Hippolitus* found to be *Virbius*, twise a man, to salue
Samela than this suppose; if they court thee with hyacinth, interteine them with roses; if he send thee a
lambe, present him an eawe; if he wooe, he wooed; and
for no other reason, but, hee is like *Maximius.* Thus she
rested, and thus she slept, all parties being equally content and satisfied with hope except *Pesana*, who fettred
with the feature of her best beloued *Menaphon* sate
cursing *Cupide* as a partiall Deitie, that would make
more daye light in the Firmament than one Sunne,
more rainebowes in the heauen than one *Iris*, and more
loues in one heart than one settled passion: manie
praiers she made to *Venus* for reuenge, manie vowes to
Cupide, manie orizons to *Hymæneus*, if shee might possesse the type of her desires. Well poore soule, howsoeuer she was paid, she smothered all with patience, and
thought to braue loue with seeming not to loue; and
thus she daily droue out the time with labour, and
looking to her heard, hearing euerie day by *Doron* who
was her kinsman, what successe *Menaphon* had in his
loues. Thus Fates and Fortune dallying a dolefull Cata-
strophe, to make a more pleasing Epitazis, it fell out
amongst them thus. *Melicertus* going to the fields, as he
was wont to doo with his flockes, droue to graze as neere
the swaines of *Menaphon* as he might, to haue a view of
his new enterteined Mistres; who, according to his ex-

pectation came thether euerie day. *Melicertus* esteeming
her to bee some Farmers daughter at the most, could
not tell how to court her: yet at length calling to rem-
brance her rare wit discouered in her last discourses,
finding opportunitie to giue her both bal and racket,
seeing the coast was cleere, and that none but *Samela*
and he were in the field, he left his flocke in the valley,
and stept vnto her, and saluted her thus.

Mistres of al eyes that glance but at the excellence of
your perfection, soueraigne of all such as *Venus* hath
allowed for louers, *Oenones* ouermatch, *Arcadies* comet,
beauties second comfort; all haile: seeing you sit like
Iuno when shee first watchte her white heyfer on the
Lincen downes, as bright as siluer *Phœbe* mounted on
the high top of the ruddie element, I was by a strange
attractiue force drawne, as the adamant draweth the
yron, or the ieat the straw, to visite your sweete selfe in
the shade, and affoord you such companie as a poore
swaine may yeeld without offence; which if you shall
vouch to deigne of, I shall be as glad of such accepted
seruice, as Paris first was of his best beloued Paramour.
Samela looking on the shepheardes face, and seeing his
vtterance full of broken sighes, thought to bee pleasant
with her shepheard thus. *Arcadies Apollo*, whose brightnesse draws euerie eye to turne as the *Heliotropion* doth
after her load; fairest of the shepheards, the Nimphes
sweetest obiect, womens wrong, in wronging manie
with ones due; welcome, and so welcome, as we vouchsafe of your seruice, admitte of your companie, as of
him that is the grace of al companies; and if we durst
vpon any light pardon, woulde venter to request you
shew vs a cast of your cunning. *Samela* made this replie,
because she heard him so superfine, as if *Ephœbus* had

learnd him to refine his mother tongue, wherefore
thought he had done it of an inkhorne desire to be eloquent; and *Melicertus* thinking that *Samela* had learnd
with *Lucilla* in *Athens* to anotamize wit, and speake
none but *Similes*, imagined she smoothed her talke to be
thought like *Sapho Phaos* Paramour. Thus deceiued
either in others suppositions, *Samela* followed her sute
thus; I know that *Priamus* wanton could not be without
flockes of Nymphes to follow him in the Vale of *Ida*,
beautie hath legions to attende her excellence if the
shepheard be true; if like *Narcissus* you wrap not
your face in the cloude of disdaine, you cannot but haue
some rare Paragon to your Mistres, whome I woulde
haue you in some sonnet describe. *Ioues* last loue, if
Ioue coulde get from *Iuno*, my pipe shal presume and I
aduenture with my voice to set out my Mistres fauour
for your excellence to censure of, and therefore thus.
Yet *Melicertus* for that hee had a farther reach, would
not make anie clownish description, chanted it thus
cunningly.

Melicertus description of his Mistres.

Tune on my pipe the praises of my Loue,
And midst thy oaten harmonie recount
How faire she is that makes thy musicke mount,
And euerie string of thy hearts harpe to moue.

Shall I compare her forme vnto the spheare
Whence Sun-bright Venus *vaunts her siluer shine?*
Ah more than that by iust compare is thine,
Whose Christall lookes the cloudie heauens doo cleare.

How oft haue I descending Titan *seene*
His burning lockes couch in the Sea-queenes lap,
And beauteous Thetis *his red bodie wrap*
In watrie roabes, as he her Lord had been.

When as my Nimph impatient of the night
Bad bright Atræus *with his traine giue place,*
Whiles she led foorth the day with her faire face,
And lent each starre a more than Delian *light.*

Not Ioue *or* Nature *should they both agree*
To make a woman of the Firmament,
Of his mixt puritie could not inuent
A Skie borne forme so beautifull as she.

When *Melicertus* had ended this roundelay in prayse
of his Mistres, *Samela* perceiued by his description,
that either some better Poet than himselfe had made it,
or else that his former phrase was dissembled: wherefore to trie him thoroughly, and to see what snake laye
hidden vnder the grasse, she followed the chase in this
manner.

Melicertus, might not a straunger craue your Mistres
name. At this the shepheard blusht, and made no reply.
How now quoth *Samela*, what is she meane that you
shame, or so high as you fear to bewray the souereign of
your thoughts? Stand not in doubt man, for be she base,
I reade that mightie *Tamberlaine* after his wife *Zeno-
crate* (the worlds faire eye) past out of the Theater of
this mortall life, he chose stigmaticall trulls to please his
humorous fancie. Be she a princesse, honour hangs in
high desires, and it is the token of a high minde to venter for a Queene: then gentle shepheard tell me thy

Mistres name. *Melicertus* hearing his goddesse speake
so fauourably, breathed out this sodaine replie; Too
high *Samela*, and therefore I feare with the *Syrian*
Wolues to barke against the Moone, or with them of
Scyrum to shoot against the starres; in the height of my
thoughts soaring too high, to fall with wofull repenting
Icarus: no sooner did mine eye glance vpon her beautie,
but as if loue and fate had sate to forge my fatall disquiet, they trapte mee within her lookes, and haling her
Idæa through the passage of my sight, placde it so deeply in the center of my heart, as maugre al my studious
indeuour it still and euer will keepe restlesse possession:
noting her vertues, her beauties, her perfections, her
excellence, and feare of her too high born parentage,
although painfully fettered, yet haue I still feared to
dare so haute an attempt to so braue a personage; least
she offensiue at my presumption, I perish in the height
of my thoughts. This conclusion broken with an abrubt
passion, could not so satisfie *Samela* but she would bee
further inquisitiue. At last after manie questions, he answered thus; seeing *Samela* I consume my selfe, and
displease you; to hazarde for the salue that maye cure
my malady, and satisfie your question, know it is the
beauteous *Samela*. Be there more of that name in *Arcady* beside my selfe quoth she. I know not qd *Melicertus*, but wer there a million, onely you are *Melicertus
Samela*. But of a million quoth she, I cannot be *Melicertus Samela*, for loue hath but one arrowe of desire in his
quiuer, but one string to his bow, and in choyce but one
aime of affection. Haue ye alreadie quoth *Melicertus* set
your rest vpõ some higher personage? No quoth *Samela*,
I meane by your selfe, for I haue hearde that your
fancie is linked alreadie to a beautiful shepherdesse in

Arcadie. At this the pore swaine tainted his cheeks with a vermillion die, yet thinking to carrie out the matter with a ieſt, he ſtood to his tackling thus; Whosoeuer *Samela* descanted of that loue, tolde you a *Canterbury* tale; some propheticall full mouth that as he were a Coblers eldeſt sonne, would by the laſte tell where an-others shooe wrings, but his sowterly aime was iuſt leuell, in thinking euerie looke was loue, or euerie faire worde a pawne of loyaltie. Then quoth *Samela* taking him at a rebound, neither may I thinke your glaunces to be fancies, nor your greateſt proteſtation any assurance of deepe affection: therefore ceasing off to court any further at this time, thinke you haue prooued your selfe a tall souldier to continue so long at batterie, and that I am a fauorable foe that haue continued so long a parley; but I charge you by the loue you owe your deereſt Mis-tres, not to say any more as touching loue for this time. If *Samela* quoth hee, thou hadſt enioyned me as *Iuno* did to *Hercules*, moſt daungerous labours, I would haue discouered my loue by obedience, and my affection by death: yet let me craue this, that as I begunne with a Sonnet, so I may ende with a Madrigale. Content *Meli-certus* quoth she, for none more than I loue Musique. Vpon this replie the shepheard proud folowed this Dittie.

Melicertus Madrigale.

What are my sheepe without their wonted food?
What is my life except I gaine my Loue?
My sheepe consume and faint for want of blood.
My life is loſt vnlesse I grace approue.
    No flower that saplesse thriues:
    No Turtle without pheare.

The day without the Sunne dooth lowre for woe,
Then woe mine eyes vnlesse they beautie see:
My Sunne Samelaes *eyes, by whom I know*
Wherein delight consists, where pleasures be.
> *Nought more the heart reuiues*
> *Than to imbrace his deare.*

The starres from earthly humors gaine their light,
Our humors by their light possesse their power:
Samelaes *eyes fedde by my weeping sight,*
Insues my paine or ioyes by smile, or lower.
> *So wends the source of loue.*
> *It feedes, it failes, it ends.*

Kinde lookes cleare to your ioy beholde her eyes,
Admire her heart, desire to taste her kisses;
In them the heauen of ioy and solace lies,
Without them evry hope his succour misses.
> *Oh how I loue to prooue*
> *Wheretoo this solace tends.*

Scarce had the shepheard ended this Madrigale, but
Samela began to frowne, saying he had broken promise.
Melicertus alledged if he had vttred any passion, twas
sung, not said. Thus these Louers in a humorous descant of their prattle espied a farre off olde *Lamedon* and
Menaphon comming towards them; wherevpon kissing
in conceipt, and parting with interchaunged glaunces,
Melicertus stole to his sheepe, and *Samela* sate her downe
making of nets to catche birds. At last *Lamedon* and her
Loue came, and after manie gracious lookes, and much
good parley, helpte her home with her sheepe, and put
them in the folds. But leauing these amorous shep-

heardes busie in their loues, let vs retourne at length to
the pretie babie *Samelas* childe, whom *Menaphō* had
put to nurse in the countrey. This infant being by Nature beautifull, and by birth noble, euen in his cradle
exprest to the eyes of the gazers such glorious presages
of his approching fortunes, as if another *Alcides* (the
arme-strong darling of the doubled night) by wrastling
with snakes in his swadling cloutes, should prophecie to
the world the approching wonders of his prowesse; so
did his fierie looks reflect terror to the weake beholders
of his ingrafted nobilitie, as if some God twise born like
vnto the *Thracian Bacchus*, forsaking his heauen borne
Deitie, shoulde delude our eyes with the alternate forme
of his infancie. Fiue yeres had full runne their monthly
reuolution, when as this beauteous boy began to shew
himselfe among the shepheards children, with whom he
had no sooner cōtracted familiar acquaintance, but
straight he was chosen Lord of the May game, king of
their sports, and ringleader of their reuils; insomuch
that his tender mother beholding him by chance mounted in his kingly maiestie, and imitating honorable
iustice in his gamesom exercise of discipline, with teares
of ioy took vp these propheticall termes; well doo I see,
where God and Fate hath vowed felicitie, no aduerse
fortune may expel prosperitie. *Pleusidippus* thou art
young, thy lookes high, and thy thoughtes hautie;
souereigntie is seated in thy eyes, and honour in thy
heart; I feare this fire will haue his flame, and then am I
vndone in thee my sonne; my countrey life (sweete
countrey life) in thy proud soaring hopes, despoyled
and disroabed of the disguised aray of his rest, must
returne russet weedes to the foldes where I lefte my
feares, and hast to the court my hell, there to inuest me

in my wonted cares. How now *Samela*, wilt thou be a *Sybil* of mishap to thy selfe? the angrie heauens that haue eternisht thy exile, haue eftablisht thy content in *Arcadie*. My content in *Arcadie*, that may not be no longer than my *Pleusidippus* ftaies in *Arcadie*, which I haue cause to feare, for the whelps of the Lion are no longer harmlesse than when they are whelpes, and babes no longer to be awed, than while they are babes. I but nature, and therewith she pawsed, being interrupted by a tumult of boies, that by yong *Pleusidippus* command fell vpon one of their fellowes, and beate him moft cruelly for playing false playe at nine holes: which she espying through her lattise window, could not chose but smile aboue measure. But when she saw him in his childish termes condemne one to death for despising the authoritie bequeathed him by the reft of the boyes, then she bethought her of the Persian *Cyrus* that deposed his Grandfather *Aftyages*, whose vse it was at like age to imitate maieftie in like manner. In this diftraction of thoughts she had not long time ftaid, but *Lamedon* and *Menaphon* calde her awaye to accompany them to the foldes, whiles *Pleusidippus* hafting to the execution of iuftice, dismissed his boyish session till their next meeting: where how imperiouslie he behaued himselfe in punishing misorders amongeft his equals, in vsing more than iefting iuftice towards his vntamed copesmates, I referre it to the Annuals of the *Arcadians* that dilate not a little of this ingenious argument. In this sort did *Pleusidippus* draw foorth his infancie, till on a time walking to the shore, where hee with his mother were wrackt, to gather cockles and pebble ftones, as children are wont: there arriued on the ftrond a *Thessalian* Pirate named *Eurilachus*, who after he had for-

F

raged in the *Arcadian* confines, driuing before him a large bootie of beasts to his ships espied this pretie infant; when gazing on his face as wanton *Ioue* gazed on *Phrygian Ganimede* in the fields of *Ida*, hee exhaled into his eyes such deepe impression of his perfection, as that his thought neuer thirsted so much after any pray, as this pretie *Pleusidippus* possession: but determining first to assay him by curtesie before hee assayled him with rigour, he began to trie his wit after this manner. My little childe, whence art thou, where wert thou borne, whats thy name, and wherefore wandrest thou thus all alone on the shoare. I pray ye what are you sir quoth *Pleusidippus*, that deale thus with me by interrogatories, as if I were some runne away. Wilt thou not tell me then who was thy father? Said he, Good sir, if ye will needes knowe goe aske that of my mother. Hath said wel my Lord quoth *Romanio* who was one of his especiall associates, for wise are the children in these dayes that know their owne fathers, especially if they be begotten in Dogge daies, when their mothers are franticke with loue, and yong men furious for lust. Besides, who knows not, that these *Arcadians* are giuen to take the benefit of euerie Hodge, when they will sacrifice their virginitie to *Venus*, though they haue but a bush of nettles for their bedde; and sure this boy is but some shepheards bastard at the most, howsoeuer his wanton face importeth more than appeerance. *Pleusidippus* eyes at this speach resolued into fire, and his face into purple, with a more than common courage in children of his yeares and stature, gaue him the lie roundly in this replie; Pesant, the bastard in thy face, for I am a Gentleman: wert thou a man in courage, as thou art a Kowe in proportion, thou wouldst neuer haue so much

empayred thy honestie, as to derogate from my honor.
Look not in my face but leuel at my heart by this that
thou seest, and therewith let driue at him with such
pebble stones as hee had in his hat, insomuch that
Romanio was driuen to his heeles, to shun this sodaine
haile shot, and *Eurilochus* resolued into a laughter, and
in tearmes of admiration most highly extolled so exceeding magnanimitie in so little a bodie; which how auaile-
able it prooued to the confirmation of his fancie, that
was before inflamed with his features, let them imagine,
that haue noted the imbecilitie of that age, and the
vnresisted furie of men at armes. Sufficeth at this instant to vnfolde (all other circumstance of praise laid
apart) that *Eurilochus* being farre in loue with his extraordinarie lineaments, awaited no farther parley, but
willed his men perforce to hoyse him a shipboord, intending as soone as euer he arriued in *Thessaly*, by
sending him to the Courte as a present, to make his
peace with his Lord and Master *Agenor*, who not long
before had proclaimed him as a notorious Pirate
throughout all his dominions. Neither swarued hee one
whit from his purpose, for no sooner had he cast anker
in the Port of *Hadrionopolis*, but he arraied him in
choyce silkes and *Tyrian* purple, and so sent him as a
prize to the King of that Country, who walking as then
in his summer garden with his Queen the beauteous
Eriphila, fell to discourse (as one well seene in Philosophie) of hearbes and flowers, as the fauour or colour did
occasion; and hauing spent sometime in disputing their
medicinable properties, his Ladie reaching him a Marigold, he began to moralize of it thus merely. I meruaile
the Poets that were so prodigall in painting the amorous
affection of the Sunne to his Hyacinth, did neuer ob-

serue the relation of loue twixt him and the Marigold:
it shoulde either seeme they were loath to incurre the
displeasure of women, by propounding it in the way of
comparison any seruile imitation for head ſtrong wiues,
that loue no precepts lesse, than those pertaining vnto
duty; or that that flower not so vsual in their gardens as
ours; in her vnacquainted name did obscure the honour
of her amors to *Apollo*; to whose motions reducing the
methode of her springing, she waketh and sleepeth,
openeth and shutteth her golden leaues, as he riseth and
setteth. Well did you foreſtall my exception quoth *Eriphila*, in terming it a seruile imitation; for were the condition of a wife so slauish as your similitude would inferre, I had as leaue be your page as your spouse, your
dogge as your darling. Not so sweete wife answered
Agenor, but the comparison holdeth in this, that as the
Marigold resembleth the Sunne both in colour and
forme, so each mans wife ought euerie way to be the
image of her husband, framing her countenance to
smile, when she sees him disposed to mirth; and con-
trariwise her eyes to teares, he being surcharged with
melancholy: and as the Marigold displaieth the orient
ornaments of her beautie to the resplendant viewe of
none but her louer *Hyperion*, so ought not a woman of
modeſtie lay open the allurements of her face to anie
but her espoused pheere; in whose absence like the
Marigold in the absence of the Sunne, she ought to
shut vp her dores, and solemnize continuall night, till
her husband her sunne making a happie return, vn-
sealeth her silence with the ioy of his sight. Beleeue me,
but if all flowers (quoth *Eriphila*) affoord such influence
of eloquence to our aduerse orators, Ile exempt them
all from my smell, for feare they be all planted to poy-

son. Ofte haue I heard (replied *Agenor*) our cunning
Phisitions conclude, that one poyson is harmelesse to
another; which if it be so, there is no cause why a thistle
should feare to be stung of a nettle. I can tell you sir,
you best were beware, least in wading too farre in comparisons of thistles and nettles, you exchange not your
rose for a nettle. If I do quoth *Agenor*, it is no more, but
my gardeners shall plucke it vp by the rootes, and throw
it ouer the wal as a weed. To end this iest that els would
issue to a iarre, what purple flower is this in forme like a
hyacinth (quoth *Eriphila*) so cunningly dropped with
bloud, as if Nature had intermedled with the Heralds
arte to emblazon a bleeding heart. It is the flower into
the which Poets doo faigne *Venus* dying *Adonis* to be
turnd, a faire boy but passing infortunate. Was it possible quoth *Eriphila*, that euer Nature should bee so
bounteous to a boy, to giue him a face in despite of
women so faire: faine would I see such an obiect, and
then would I defie beautie, for imparting our excellencie
to any inferiour abiect. In saying these words (as if
Fortune meant to present her fancie with his desired
felicitie) *Romanio* conducted by one of the Lords came
with yong *Pleusidippus* in his hand into the priuie garden: where discoursing vnto the king the intent of
Eurilochus in presenting him with such an inestimable
Iewell, the manner of his taking in the Strond of *Arcadie*, with other circumstance of vowed alleageance; all
which being gratefully accepted of *Agenor*, he sealed
their seuerall pardons, and so gaue them leaue to depart. But when he had throughly obserued euerie perfection of yong *Pleusidippus*, he burst into these tearmes
of passion; Had sea-borne *Pontia* then an appliable eare
in our idlenesse, that to testifie hir eternall deitie, she

should send vs a second *Adonis* to delude our senses?
What euer may deserue the name of faire haue I seen
before, beautie haue I beheld in his brigheſt orb, but
neuer set eye on immortalitie before this houre. *Eriphila*
likewise in no lesse extasie, seeing her eyes to dazle with
the reflexe of his beautie, and hir cheekes tainted with a
blush of disgrace by too too much gazing on his face,
said; that eyther the Sunne had lefte his bower to beguile their eyes with a borrowed shape (which could not
keepe in his brightnesse) or *Cupide* dismounted from
his mothers lappe, left his bow and quiuer at randon, to
outbraue the *Thessalian* dames in their beautie. In this
contrarietie of thoughts, being all plunged welnigh in a
speachlesse aſtonishment, the faire childe *Pleusidippus*
not vsed to such hyperbolical spectators, broke off the
silence by calling for his victualls, as one whose emptie
ſtomack since his comming from sea, was not ouer-
cloyed with delicates, whereat *Agenor* reuiued from his
trance, wherein the present wonder had inwrapt him,
demanded such queſtions of his name and parentage as
the Pirates ignorance could not vnfold; but he being
able to tel no more than this, that his mother was a shepheardesse, and his owne name *Pleusidippus*, cut off all
their further interrogatories by calling after his childish
manner againe for his dinner. Whereupon *Agenor* commanding him to be had in, and vsed in euerie respect as
the childe of a Prince, began in his solitarie walke by
his countenance to calculate his Natiuitie, and measure
his birth by his beautie, contracting him in thought
heyre to his kingdome of *Thessaly*, and husbande to his
daughter, before he knewe whence the childe descended, or who was his father.

But leauing yong *Pleusidippus* thus spending his

youth in the *Thessalian* Court, protected with the tender
affection of such a courteous Foster-father as *Agenor*;
returne wee where we lefte backe vnto *Arcadie*, and
meete his Mother the faire *Samela* returning from the
foldes: who hauing discoursed by the way as she came
home to *Lamedon* and *Menaphon* what shee late sawe
and obserued in her sonne, they both conioyned their
iudgements to this conclusion, that hee was doubtles
borne to some greater fortunes than the sheepcoates
could containe, and therefore it behooued her to further
his Destinies with some good and liberall education,
and not to detaine him any longer in that trade of life,
which his fortune withstood: but by the way to rebuke
him for tyrannising so Lorldlie ouer the boies, least the
neighbor shepheards might happely intrude the name
of iniurie on them being strangers for his insulting ouer
their children. With this determination came she home,
and calling for *Pleusidippus* according to their former
counsaile, he would in no wise be found. Thereupon
enquirie was made amongest all the shepheards, diligent search in euerie village, but stil the most careful-
lest post returned with *Non est inuentus*. Which *Samela*
hearing, thinking she had vtterly lost him whome Fortune had saued, began in this manner to act her vnrest;
Dissembling heauens, where is your happinesse? vn-
constant times, what are your triumphes? haue you
therefore hethertoo fed me with honie, that you might
at last poyson me with gall? Haue you fatted mee so long
with *Sardenian* smiles, that like the wracke of the *Syrens*,
I might perrish in your wiles? Curst that I was to affie
in your curtesie, curst that am to taste of your crueltie.
O *Pleusidippus*, liuest thou, or art thou dead? No thou
art dead, dead to the world, dead to thy kinsfolkes, dead

to *Cipres*, dead to *Arcadie*, dead to thy mother *Samela*;
and with thee dies the worlds wonder, thy kinsfolkes
comfort, *Cipres* soule, *Arcadies* hopes, thy mothers honours. Was this the prophecie of thy souereigntie, to
yeeld vp thy life to death so vntimely? wretched was I of
al women to bring thee foorth to this infancie. O cruel
Themis that didſt reuolue such vneuitable fate; hard
harted death to prosecute me with such hate. Haue wee
therefore escapte the furie of the seas, to perish on the
land? was it not inough that we were exiled from higher
prosperitie, but we muſt all of vs thus sodainly be ouer-
whelmed with the ouerflowe of a second aduersitie? my
husband and thy father to be swalowed in the furie of
the surge, and now thou to bee (and therewith her eyes
diſtilled such abundance of teares, as ſtopt the passage
of her plaints, and made her seeme a more than second
Niobe, bewailing her seauen fold sorrow vnder the forme
of a weeping Flint.) *Menaphon* who had ouer heard her
all this while, as one that sought opportunitie to plead
his vnreſt, perceiuing her in that extremitie of agonie
for hir sons supposed losse, ſtept to hir presently, and
cheerde hir vp in these tearmes; Faire shepheardesse,
might the teares of contrition raise the dead from de-
ſtruction, then were it wisedome to bewaile what weeping might recall; but since such anguish is fruitelesse,
and these plainings bootlesse; comfort your self with
the hope of the liuing, and omit the teares for the dead.
Why quoth *Samela* how is it possible a woman should
loose him without griefe, whom she hath conceiued
with sorrow: he was sweete *Menaphon*, the diuided halfe
of my essence, soule to my ioyes, and life to my delights;
as beauteous in his birth, as is our bright bow-bearing
God, that played the shepheard awhile for loue, amid-

dest our pleasant *Arcadian* Downes. What ere hee was
in beautie quoth *Menaphon*, proceeded from your bountie; who may by marriage make his like when you
please: therefore there is no cause you shuld so much
grieue to see your first worke defacde, that of a newe
molde can forme a farre better than euer he was. Ah
Menaphon, nere more may his like proceede from my
loynes; I tell thee he made the chamber bright with his
beautie when he was born, and chacte the night with
the golden rayes that gleamed from his lookes: nere
more may I bee the mother of such a sonne. Yes *Samela*
(quoth the frolicke shephearde) thinke not but if thou
wilt list to my loues, I will enrich thee with as faire
increase as euer he was. Alas pore swaine said she, thou
hopest in vaine, since another must reape what thou
hast sowne, and gather into his barnes what thou hast
scattered in the furrowe. Another reape what I haue
sowen: therwith he scracht his head where it icht not,
and setting his cap he could not tell which way, in a hot
fustian fumes he vttred these words of furie; Strumpet
of *Greece*, repaiest thou my loue with this lauish ingratitude? haue I therefore with my plentie supplied thy
wants, that thou with thy pride shouldst procure my
wo? did I relieue thee in distresse, to wound me in thy
welfare with disdaine? deceitfull woman (and therewith
hee swore a holiday oath, by *Pan* the God of the Shepheards) either returne loue for loue, or I will turne thee
forth of doores to scrape vp thy crummes where thou
canst; and make thee pitied for thy pouertie, that earst
while wert honoured in euerie mans eye through the
supportance of thy beautie. Belike then quoth *Samela*,
when you intertained me into your house, you did it not
in regarde of the lawes of hospitalitie, but onely with

this policie to quench the flames of your fancie: then
sir haue I mistooke your honestie, and am lesse indebted to your courtesie. Nay I thought no lesse said
Menaphon, when your straggling eye at our last meeting
would be gadding throughout euerie corner of our companie, that you would proue such a kinde kistrell; but if
you will needes bee starting, Ile serue yee thereafter I
warrant you: then see which of our beardlesse yongsters
will take ye in, when I haue cast you foorth. Those
quoth shee that countenance *Menaphon* and his pelfe,
and are better able than your selfe: but howsoeuer I
finde their fauour, I henceforth defie you and your fel-
lowship. And therewith in great rage she flũg away into
the next chamber, where her vncle *Lamedon* laye a sleepe;
to whome complaining of *Menaphons* discurtesies, he
straight inuented this remedie; there was a shepheard
called *Moron* (brother to *Doron*) that not long before
died of a surfet, whose house and flocke beeing set to
sale after his decease, he bought them both foorthwith
for *Samela* with certaine remainder of money he had,
and therein enfeaft her maugre the furie of *Menaphon*;
who when hee saw she was able to support her state
without his purse, became sicke for anger, and spent
whole Eclogues in anguish. Sometime lying comfortlesse on his bedde he would complaine him to the
windes of his woes, in these or such like woords; Forlorne, and forsooke since Phisicke dooth loathe thee;
despaire be thy death, Loue is a God and despiseth thee
a man; Fortune blinde, and can not beholde thy de-
sertes: die, die, fonde *Menaphon*, that vngratefully hast
abandoned thy Mistresse. And therewith stretching
himselfe vppon his bedde, as thinking to haue slept, hee
was restrained by cares that exiled all rest from his eyes:

whereuppon taking his pipe in his hande, twixte playing and singing hee playned him thus.

Menaphons Song in his bedde.

You reſtlesse cares companions of the night,
That wrap my ioyes in folds of endlesse woes:
Tyre on my heart, and wound it with your spight,
Since Loue and Fortune proues my equall foes.
     Farewell my hopes, farewell my happie daies:
     Welcome sweete griefe, the subiect of my laies.

Mourne heauens, mourne earth, your shepheard is forlorne;
Mourne times and houres since bale inuades my bowre:
Curse euerie tongue the place where I was borne,
Curse euerie thonght the life which makes me lowre.
     Farewell my hopes, farewell my happie daies,
     Welcome sweete griefe the subiect of my laies.

Was I not free? was I not fancies aime?
Framde not desire my face to front disdaine?
I was; she did: but now one silly maime
Makes me to droope as he whom loue hath slaine.
     Farewell my hopes, farewell my happie daies,
     Welcome sweete griefe the subiect of my layes.

Yet drooping, and yet liuing to this death,
I sigh, I sue for pitie at her shrine,
Whose fierie eyes exhale my vitall breath,
And make my flockes with parching heate to pine.
     Farewell my hopes, farewell my happie daies,
     Welcome sweete griefe the subiect of my layes.

Fade they, die I, long may she liue to blisse
That feedes a wanton fire with fuell of her forme,
And makes perpetuall summer where shee is;
Whiles I doo crie oretooke with enuies storme,
  Farewell my hopes, farewell my happie daies:
  Welcome sweete griefe, the subiect of my laies.

No sooner had *Menaphon* ended this dittie, but *Pesana* hearing that he was lately falne sicke, and that *Samela* and hee were at mortall iarres; thinking now to make hay while the Sunne shinde, and take opportunitie by his forelockes, comming into his chamber vnder pretence to visite him, fell into these tearmes; Why how now *Menaphon*, hath your newe change driuen you to a night cap? Beleeue me this is the strangest effect of loue that euer I saw, to freeze so quicklye the heart it set on fire so lately. Why maye it not bee a burning feuer as well quoth *Menaphon* blushing? Nay that can not be said *Pesana*, since you shake for cold, not swelt for heat. Why if it be so it is long of cold interteinment. Why quoth *Pesana*, hath your hot intertainment cooled your courage? No, but her vndeserued hate quite hindered my conquest. You knowe quoth *Pesana* where you might haue been let in long ere this, without either assalt or anie such battrie. With this the shephearde was mute and *Pesana* ashamed: but at length regathering his spirites to bewray his martyrdome, and make his olde Mistresse some new musicke, he strained foorth this dittie.

Faire fields proud Floras *vaunt, why is't you smile*
     when as I languish?
You golden meads, why striue you to beguile
     my weeping anguish?

I liue to sorrow, you to pleasure spring:
                    why doo you spring thus?
What will not Boreas *tempeſts wrathfull king*
                    take some pitie on vs?
And send foorth Winter in hir ruſtie weede,
                    to waite my bemonings;
Whiles I diſtreſt doo tune my countrey reede
                    vnto my gronings.
But heauen, and earth, time, place, and euerie power
                    haue with her conspired
To turne my blissefull sweetes to balefull sower,
                    since fond I desired
The heauen whereto my thoughts may not aspire:
                    ay me vnhappie.
It was my fault t'imbrace my bane the fire
                    that forceth me die.
Mine be the paine, but hirs the cruell cause
                    of this ſtrange torment:
Wherefore no time my banning praiers shall pause,
                    till proud she repent.

Well I perceiue quoth *Pesana,* for all she hath let you flie like a Hawke that hath loſt hir tyre; yet you meane to follow sute and seruice, though you get but a handfull of smoake to the bargaine. Not so quoth *Menaphon,* but perhaps I seek to returne an ill bargaine as deare as I bought it. If you doo so, you are wiser than this kercher dooth shew you quoth *Pesana.* Much idle prattle to this purpose had *Menaphō* with *Pesana* in his sicknesse, and long it was not, but that with good diet and warme broths, (and especially by her carefull attendance) hee began to gather vp his crummes, and liſten by litle and litle to the loue he late scorned. Leaue we them

to their equall desires, as surfetting either of others societie; and let vs looke back to *Thessaly*, where *Samelaes*
stripling (now growne vp to the age of sixteene yeres)
flourisht in honour and feates of armes aboue all the
Knights of the Court, insomuch that the eccho of his
Fame, was the onely newes talkt on throughout euerie
towne in *Greece*: but *Olympia* the Mistres of his prowesse, (for so was the Kings daughter named) was she
that most of all exalted in the farre renowmed reports of
his martiall perfections, to whose praise hee did conse-
crate al his indeuours, to whose exquisite forme he did
dedicate all his aduentures. But hell-borne Fame, the
eldest daughter of *Erinnis*, enuying the felicitie of these
two famous Louers, dismounted eftsoones from hir
brasse sounding buildings, and vnburdened hir selfe of
hir secrets in the presence of yong *Pleusidippus*, among
whose catalogue she had not forgot to discouer, the in-
comparable beautie of the *Arcadian* shepheardesse;
whereof the young Prince no sooner had receiued an
inckling, but he stood vpon thornes til he had satisfied
his desire with her sight. Therefore on a time sitting
with his Mistresse at supper, when for table talke it was
debated amongst them, what Countrey bredde the most
accomplisht Dames for all thiugs? After straungers and
others had deliuered vp their opinions without parcial-
itie, one amongst them all who had been in *Arcadie*,
gaue vp his verdit thus freely; Gentlewomen (quoth hee)
bee it no disgrace for the Moone to stoope to the Sunne,
for the starres to giue place when *Titan* appeares; then
I hope neither the *Thessalians* will be moued, nor the
Grecians agrieued, if I make *Apollos Arcadie* beauties
Meridian. Neither wil I proceede heerein as our Philosophicall Poets are wont, that muster euerie moouer in

the Zodiacke, euerie fixed starre in the firmament, euerie elementall worde of arte in an Almanacke, to prooue
that Countrey for beautie most Canonicall where their
Mistresse abideth; when as God wot, had they but
learned of *Appelles, Ne sutor vltra crepidam*, they wold
not haue aspired aboue their birth, or talkt beyond their
sowterly bringing vp. Our *Arcadian* Nimphs are faire
and beautifull, though not begotten of the Suns bright
rayes; whose eyes vant loues armorie to the viewe,
whose angelical faces are to the obscure earth in steed
of a Firmament: viewe but this counterfeite (and therewithall hee shewed the picture of *Samela*) and see if it
be not of force to draw the Sunne from his spheare, or
the Moone from hir circle to gaze as the one did on the
beautie of *Daphne*, or al night contemplate as the other
on the forme of *Endymion, Pleusidippus* who al this
while heard his tale with attentiue patience, no sooner
beheld the radiant glory of this resplendant face, but as
a man alreadie installed in eternitie, he exclaimed thus
abruptly, O *Arcadie, Arcadie* storehouse of Nimphs, and
nurserie of beautie. At which words *Olympia* starting vp
suddenly, as if she a second *Iuno*, had taken hir *Ioue* in
bed with *Alcmena*: and ouercasting the chamber with a
frown that was able to mãtle the world with an eternall
night, she made passage to her choller in these termes
of contempt; Beardlesse vpstart of I know not whence,
haue the fauours of my bounty (not thy desert) entred
thee so deeply in ouerweening presumption, that thou
shouldst be the formost in derogation of our dignitie,
and blaspheming of my beautie? I tell thee recreant, I
scorne thy clownish *Arcady* with his inferiour comparisons, as one that prizeth her perfection aboue anie created constitution. *Pleusidippus* vpon this speach stood

plunged in a great perplexitie whether he should excuse himselfe mildly, or take her vp roundly: but the latter being more leuel to his humor thã the former, he begun thus to rowze vp his furie; Disdainful dame that vpbraidest me with my birth as it were base, and my youth as it were boyish, know that although my parents and progenie are enuied by obscuritie, yet the sparkes of renown that make my Eagle minded thoughts to mount, the heauēly fire imprisoned in the pannicles of my crest, inciting me to more deeds of honor, than stout *Perseus* effected with his fauchon in the fields of *Hesperia*, assertaineth my soule I was the sonne of no coward, but a Gentleman: but since my inequalitie of parentage, is such an eye sore to thy enuie, holde take thy fauors, (and therewith he threw her her gloue) and immortalize whom thou wilt with thy toyes; for I will to *Arcadie* in despite of thee and thine affinitie, there either to seeke out mischance, or a new Mistres. With this in a great rage he rose from the boord, and would have mounted himselfe to depart in that mood, had not the Lords and gentlemen there present disswaded him from such an vnaduised enterprise. Neither was this vnkindnesse kept so secret, but it came to the Kings eare as he was new rise from dinner; who for the loue he bare to *Pleusidippus* whome hee had honoured with Knighthood not long before, and for the toward hopes he saw in him, tooke paines to goe to the chamber where they were; and finding his daughter in straunge manner perplexed with the thought of *Pleusidippus* departure, her eyes red, and her cheekes all to be blubbered with her iealous teares, he tooke her vp in this manner. Daughter, I thought I had chose such a one to be the obiect of your eie, as you might haue euerie way loued and honoured as the Lord of your life, and not haue controlled as the slaue of your luste. Did I therefore grace him with my countenance, that you should distaine him with your taunts; peeuish girle, I aduise thee on my displeasure, either reconcile thy selfe betimes, and reforme thy vn-reuerent tearmes, or I will disclaime the loue of a Father, and deale by thee no more as a daughter. *Olympia* who alreadie had sufficiently bitten on the bridle, took these words more vnkindly than all her former bitternesse, which she disgested but sowerly; neuerthe-lesse making necessitie the present times best pollicie, shee humbled her selfe as shee might with modestie, and desired the best interpretation of what was past: *Pleusidippus* whose courteous inclination coulde not withstand this submission, in sign of reconcilement gaue her a *stoccado des labies:* yet was he not so recon-ciled, but he kept on his purpose of going to *Arcadie*; whereat *Olympia* (although she grudged inwardly, yet being loath to offend) helde her peace, and determined to bestowe vppon him a remembrance, whereby he might bee brought to thinke vppon her in his absence; which was the deuise of a bleeding heart floting in the sea, waues curiouslie stampt in golde, with this *Motto* about it, *Portum aut mortem*; alluding as it seemed to the deuise in his shield, wherein (because he was taken vp by *Eurilochus* on the shore) was cunningly drawne in a field argent, the sea waues with *Venus* sitting on the top, in token that his affection was alreadie fettered. Here holde this said she my sweet *Pleusidippus*, and hang it about thy neck, that when thou art in *Arcadie* it may be euer in thine eye; so shall these droppes of ruth that paint out a painfull trueth, withdraw thy fancie from attracting strange beautie: which said, the teares gusht

G

from her eyes, and good *Agenors* likewise, who gaue
him nothing so much in charge, as to make haſt of his
returne. *Pleusidippus* although he could haue bin content to haue done the like for companie, yet he had such
a minde on his iourney, that he broke off such ceremonies, and haſted a shipboord; and in a Barke bounde
for *Arcadie*, hauing the winde fauourable made a short
cut, so that in a daye and nights sayling, he arriued on
the shore adioyning to the Promontorie wher he, his
mother, and his vnckle *Lamedon* were firſt wrackt.

Leaue we him wandring with some few of his traine
that came with him alongſt the sea side, to seeke out
some town or village where to refresh themselues; and
let vs awhile to the Court of *Democles* where our Historie began: who hauing committed his daughter with
her tender babe, her husbande *Maximius*, and *Lamedon*
his vnckle without oare or mariner to the furie of the
merciles waues, determined to leaue the succession of
his kingdome to vncertaine chance: for his Queene with
Sepheſtiaes losse (whŏ she deemed to be dead) tooke
such thought, that within short time after she died
Democles as carelesse of all weathers, spent his time
Epicure-like in all kinde of pleasures that either art or
expence might affoord; so that for his dissolute life he
seemed another *Heliogabalus*, deriuing his securitie from
that grounded tranquilitie, which made it prouerbiall to
the world, *No heauen but Arcadie*. Hauing spent manie
yeares in this varietie of vanitie, Fame determining to
applye her selfe to his fancie, sounded in his eares the
singular beautie of his daughter *Samela*; he, although
he were an olde colte, yet had not caſt all his wanton
teeth, which made him vnder the brute of beeing sick
of a grieuous appoplexie, ſteale from his Court secretly

in the disguise of a shepheard, to come and seek out
Samela; who not a little proud of hir new flocke, liude
more contented than if she had been Queene of *Arcadie;*
and *Melicertus* ioying not a little that shee was parted
from *Menaphon*, vsed euerie day to visite her without
dread, and courte her in such shepheards tearmes as he
had; which howe they pleased her I leaue to you to
imagine, when as not long after she vowed mariage to
him solemnly in presence of all the shepheards, but not
to be solemnized till the Prophecie was fulfilled, mentioned in the beginning of this Historie. Although this
penance exceeded the limits of his patience; yet hoping
that the Oracle was not vttered in vaine, and might as
well (albeit he knew not which way) bee accomplished
in him as in any other, was contented to make a vertue
of necessitie, and await the vtmost of his destinie. But
Pleusidippus, who by this time had perfected his polli-
cies, exchaunging his garments with one of the heardgroomes of *Menaphon*, tracing ouer the Plaines in the
habit of a Shepheard, chanced to meete with *Democles* as
he was new come into those quarters; whom mistaking
for an olde shepheard, he began many impertinent questions belonging to the Sheepecoates, at last he askt him
if he knew *Samelas* sheepfold; who answering doubt-
fully vnto all alike, made him halfe angrie: and had not
Samela past by at that instant to fill her bottle at a
spring neere the foote of the Promontorie, he should
lyke inough haue had first hansell of our new Shepheards sheepe-hooke. But the wonder of her beautie so
wrought with his wounded fancie, that he thought report a partiall spreader of her praises, and fame too base
to talke of such formes. *Samela* espying this faire shepheard so farre ouer-gone in his gazing, stept to him, and

askt him if he knew her that hee so ouerlookt her. Pardon me faire shepheardesse (quoth *Pleusidippus*) if it be a fault, for I cannot chuse being Eagle sighted but gaze on the Sunne the first time I see it. And truely I cannot chuse but compare you to one of *Æsops* Apes, that finding a Gloworme in the night, tooke it for fire; and you seeing a face full of deformities, mistake it for the Sunne. Indeede it maye be mine eyes made opposite to such an obiect may faile in their office, hauing their lights rebated by such brightnesse. Nay not vnlike quoth *Samela*, for els out of doubt you would see your way better. Why quoth *Pleusidippus* I cannot go out of the way, when I meete such glistering Goddesses in my way. How now sir *Paris*, are you out of your Arithmeticke, I thinke you haue lost your witts with your eyes, that mistake *Arcadie* for Ida, and a Shepheardesse for a Goddes. How euer it please you (quoth *Pleusidippus*) to derogate from my prowesse by the title of *Paris*, know that I am not so farre out of my Arithmetick, but that by Multiplication I can make two of one, in an houres warning, or bee as good as a cypher to fill vp a place at the worst hand; for my wit sufficeth be it neuer so simple to proue both *re* and *voce* that there can be no *vacuum in rerum natura*, and mine eyes (or else they deceiue me) will enter so farre in arte, as *niger est contrarius albo*, and teach mee how to discerne twixt blacke and white. Much other circumstaunce of prattle passed betweene them, which the *Arcadian* Records doo not shew, nor I remember; sufficeth he pleaded loue, and was repulst: which droue him into such a cholar, that meeting his supposed shepheard, (who lying vnder a bush, had all this while ouer heard them) he entred into such termes of indignation, as *Ioue* shaking his earthquaking haire,

when he sate in consultation of *Licaon*. Wherefore *Democles* perceiuing *Pleusidippus* repulst, who was euery
way gracde with the ornaments of Nature, began to cast
his bad peniworths, in whose face age had furrowed her
wrinckles; except hee should lay his crowne at her feete,
and tell her he was King of *Arcadia*; which in Cōmon
wealths respectes, seeming not commodious, he thought
to turne a new leafe, and make this yong shepheard the
meanes to perfect his purpose. Hee had not farre from
that place a strong Castle, which was inhabited as then
by none but tilsmen and heardgroomes: thether did he
perswade *Pleusidippus* to carrie her perforce, and effect
that by cōstraint, that he could not atchieue by intreatie;
who listning not a little to this counsaile, that was neuer
platted for his aduantage, presently put in practise what
he of late gaue in precepts, and waiting till the euening
that *Samela* should fold hir sheep, hauing giuen his men
the watch word, maugre al the shepheards adioyning he
mounted her behind him; and being by *Democles* direct-
ed to the Castle, he made such hauocke among the stub-
borne heardsmen, that wil they nill they, he was Lord of
the Castle. Yet might not all this preuaile with *Samela*,
who constant to her olde shephearde, would not interteine anie new loue; which made *Pleusidippus* thinke all
his haruest lost in the reaping, and blemisht al his delights with a mournful drooping. But *Democles* that
lookt for a mountaine of golde in a Mole hill, finding
her all alone, began to discourse his loue in more ample
mauner thã euer *Pleusidippus*, telling her how he was a
King, what his reuenewes were, what power he had to
aduance her; with many other proud vaunts of his
wealth, and prodigal termes of his treasure. *Samela*
hearing the name of a King, and perceiuing him to be

hir Father, stoode amazed like *Medusaes* Metamorphosis, and blushing oft with intermingled sighes, began to
thinke how iniurious fortune was to her showen in such
an incestuous father. But he hot spurred in his purpose,
gaue hir no time to deliberate, but required either a
quicke consent, or a present deniall. She tolde him, that
the Shepheard *Melicertus* was alreadie intitled in the in-
terest of hir beautie, wherefore it was in vain what he or
anie other could plead in the way of perswasion. He
thereupon entring into a large field of the basenesse of
Shepheards, and royalties of Kings, with manie other
assembled arguments of delight, that would haue fetcht
Venus from her sphere to disport: but *Samela* whose
mouth could disgest no other meate saue onely hir
sweete *Melicertus*, ashamed so long to holde parley with
her father about such a matter, flung away to her withdrawing chamber in a dissembled rage, and there after
her wonted manner bewailed her misfortunes.

   Democles plunged thus in a Laborinth of restles passions, seeing *Melicertus* figure was so deepely printed in
the center of her thoughts, as neither the resolution of
his fancie, his Metamorphosis from a King to a trau-
eler, Crownes, Kingdomes, preferments, (battries that
soone ouerthrowe the fortresse of womens fantasies)
when *Democles* I saye, saw that none of these colde re-
mooue *Samela*; hearing that the *Arcadian* shepheardes
were in a vprore for the losse of their beautiful shepheardesse, his hot loue changing to a bird of coye disdaine; he intended by some reuenge, either to obtaine
his loue, or satisfie his hate: whereupon throughly resolued, he stole away secretly in his shepheards apparaile, and got him down to the Plaines; where he found
all the swains in a mutinie about the recouerie of their

beautifull Paragon. *Democles* stepping amongst the
route, demanded the cause of their controuersie. Marie
sir quoth *Doron* bluntly, the flower of all our garland is
gone. How meane you that sir, quoth he? We had answered *Doron*, an Eaw amongst our Ramms, whose
fleece was as white as the haires that grow on father
Boreas chinne, or as the dangling deawlap of the siluer
Bull, her front curled like to the *Erimanthian* Boare, and
spangled like the woosted stockings of *Saturne*, her face
like *Mars* treading vpon the milke white cloudes: beleeue me shepheard, her eyes were like the fierie torches
tilting against the Moone: this paragon, this none such,
this Eaw, this Mistres of our flockes, was by a wily Foxe
stolne from our foldes; for which these shepheards as-
semble themselues, to recouer so wealthie a prize. What
is he quoth *Menaphō* that *Doron* is in such debate with?
Fellowe canst thou tell vs anie newes of the faire shepheardesse, that the Knight of *Thessaly* hath carried away
from her fellow Nymphes. *Democles* thinking to take
opportunitie by the forhead: and seeing Time had feathered his bolte, willing to assaye as hee might to hit the
marke, began thus.

Shepheardes, you see my profession is your trade,
and although my wandring fortunes be not like your
home borne fauours; yet were I in the groues of *Thessalian Tempe*, as I am in the plaines of *Arcadie*, the
swaines would giue mee as manie due honors, as they
present you here with submisse reuerence. Beautie that
drew *Apollo* from heauen to playe the shepheard, that
fetcht *Ioue* from heauen to bear the shape of a Bul for
Agenors daughter, the excellence of such a Metaphu-
sicall vertue, I meane shepheard the fame of your faire
Samela, houering in the eares of euerie man as a miracle

of nature, brought me from *Thessaly* to feede mine eyes
with *Arcadies* wonder: stepping alongst the shoare to
come to some sheepecoate where my wearie limmes
might haue rest, Loue that for my labors thought to
lead me to fancies pauilion, was my conduct to a castle,
where a *Thessalian* knight lyes in holde, the Portcullis
was let downe, the bridge drawen, the Court of garde
kept, thether I went; and for by my tongue I was known
to be a *Thessalian*, I was enterteined and lodged: the
Knight whose yeares are young, and valure matchlesse,
holding in his armes a Ladie more beautifull thã Loues
Queene, all blubbered with teares, asked me manie
questions, which as I might I replide vnto: but while he
talkt, mine eye surfetting with such excellence, was de-
tained vpon the glorious shew of such a wonderfull obiect; I demanded what she was of the standers by, and
they said she was the faire shepheardesse whome the
Knight had taken from the swaines of *Arcadie*, and
woulde carrie with the first winde that serued into *Thessaly:* This shepheards I knowe, and grieue that thus
your loues should be ouermatcht with Fortune, and
your affections pulde backe by contrarietie of Destinie.
Melicertus hearing this, the fire sparkling out of his eyes
began thus; I tell thee shephearde, if Fates with their
forepointing pencels did pen down, or Fortune with her
deepest varietie resolue, or Loue with his greatest power determine to depriue *Arcadie* of the beautifull *Samela*,
we would with our blood signe downe such spels on the
Plaines, that either our Gods should summon her to
Elizium, or shee rest with vs quiet and fortunate: thou
seest the shepheardes are vp in armes to reuenge, onely
it rests who shall haue the honour and principalitie of
the field. What needs that questiõ quoth *Menaphon*, am

not I the Kings shepheard, and chiefe of all the border-
ing swaines of *Arcadie*. I grant quoth *Melicertus*, but am
not I a Gentleman, though tirde in shepheardes skin-
coate; superiour to thee in birth, though equall nowe in
profession. Well from words they had falne to blowes,
had not the shepheards parted them; and for the auoyd-
ing of farther troubles, it was agreed that they should in
two Eclogs make description of their loue, and *Democles*, for he was a stranger, to sit Censor, and who best
could decipher his Mistres perfection, should be made
Generall of the rest. *Menaphon* and *Melicertus* condes-
cended to this motion, and *Democles* sitting as Iudge,
the rest of the shepheards standing as witnesses of this
combat *Menaphon* began thus.

Menaphons Eclogue.

Too weake the wit, too slender is the braine
That meanes to marke the power and worth of loue;
Not one that liues (except he hap to proue)
Can tell the sweete, or tell the secret paine.

Yet I that haue been prentice to the griefe,
Like to the cunning sea-man from a farre,
By gesse will talke the beautie of that starre,
Whose influence must yeeld me chiefe reliefe.

You Censors of the glorie of my deare,
With reuerence and lowlie bent of knee,
Attend and marke what her perfections bee:
For in my words my fancies shall appeare.

Hir lockes are pleighted like the fleece of wooll
That Iason *with his* Gretian *mates atchiude,*
As pure as golde, yet not from golde deriude;
As full of sweetes, as sweete of sweetes is full.

Her browes are pretie tables of conceate,
Where Loue his records of delight dooth quoate,
On them her dallying lockes doo daily floate
As Loue full oft dooth feede vpon the baite.

Her eyes, faire eyes, like to the purest lights
That animate the Sunne, or cheere the day,
In whom the shining Sun-beames brightly play
Whiles fancie dooth on them diuine delights.

Hir cheekes like ripened lillies steept in wine,
Or faire pomegranade kernels washt in milke,
Or snow white threds in nets of crimson silke,
Or gorgeous cloudes vpon the Sunnes decline.

Her lips are roses ouerwasht with dew,
Or like the purple of Narcissus *flower:*
No frost their faire, no winde doth wast their power,
But by her breath her beauties doo renew.

Hir christall chin like to the purest molde,
Enchac'de with daintie daysies soft and white,
Where fancies faire pauilion once is pight,
Where as imbrac'de his beauties he doth holde.

Hir necke like to an yuorie shining tower
Where through with azure veynes sweete Nectar *runnes,*
Or like the downe of Swannes *where* Senesse *woons,*
Or like delight that doth it selfe deuoure.

Hir pappes are like faire apples in the prime,
As round as orient pearles, as soft as downe:
They neuer vaile their faire through winters frowne,
But from their sweetes Loue suckt his summer time.

Hir bodie beauties best esteemed bowre,
Delicious, comely, daintie, without staine:
The thought whereof (not touch) hath wrought my paine.
Whose faire, all faire and beauties doth deuoure.

Hir maiden mount, the dwelling house of pleasure;
Not like, for why no like surpasseth wonder:
O blest is he may bring such beauties vnder,
Or search by sute the secrets ofthat treasure.

Deuourd in thought, how wanders my deuice,
What rests behind I must deuine vpon?
Who talkes the best, can say but fairer none:
Few words well coucht doo most content the wise.

All you that heare; let not my sillie stile
Condemne my zeale: for what my tongue should say
Serues to inforce my thoughts to seeke the way
Whereby my woes and cares I doo beguile.

Selde speaketh Loue, but sighs his secret paines;
Teares are his truce-men, words doo make him tremble.
How sweete is loue to them that can dissemble
In thoughts and lookes, till they haue reapt the gaines,

Alonely I am plaine, and what I say
I thinke, yet what I thinke tongue cannot tell:
Sweete Censors take my silly worst for well:
My faith is firme, though homely be my laye.

After the haples *Menaphon* had in this homely discourse shadowed his heauenly delight; the shepheard
Melicertus after some pause began in this sort.

Melicertus Eclogue.

What neede compare where sweete exceedes compare?
Who drawes his thoughts of loue from senselesse things,
Their pompe and greateſt glories doth impaire,
And mounts Loues heauen with ouer leaden wings.

Stones, hearbes and flowers, the foolish spoyles of earth,
Flouds, mettalls, colours, dalliance of the eye:
These shew conceipt is ſtaind with too much dearth:
Such abſtract fond compares make cunning die.

But he that hath the feeling taſte of Loue
Deriues his essence from no earthlie toy;
A weake conceipt his power cannot approue,
For earthly thoughts are subieɗ to annoy.

Be whiſt, be ſtill, be silent Censers now;
My fellow swaine has tolde a pretie tale
Which moderne Poets may perhaps allow,
Yet I condemne the tearmes; for they are ſtale.

Apollo *when my Miſtres firſt was borne*
Cut off his lockes, and left them on hir head,
And said; I plant these wires in Natures scorne,
Whose beauties shall appeare when Time is dead.

From foorth the Chriſtall heauen when she was made,
The puritie thereof did taint hir brow:
On which the gliſtering Sunne that sought the shade
Gan set, and there his glories doth auow.

Those eyes, faire eyes, too faire to be describde,
Were those that earst the Chaos did reforme:
To whom the heauen their beauties haue ascribde,
That fashion life in man, in beast, in worme.

When first hir faire delicious cheekes were wrought,
Aurora brought hir blush, the Moone hir white:
Both so combinde as passed Natures thought,
Compilde those pretie orbes of sweete delight.

When Loue and Nature once were proud with play,
From both their lips hir lips the Corall drew:
On them doth fancy sleepe, and euerie day
Doth swallow ioy such sweete delights to view.

Whilome while Venus Sonne did seeke a bowre
To sport with Psiches his desired deare,
He chose her chinne; and from that happie stowre
He neuer stints in glorie to appeare.

Desires and Ioyes that long had serued Loue,
Besought a Holde where pretie eyes might woo them:
Loue made her necke, and for their best behoue
Hath shut them there, whence no man can vndoo them.

Once Venus dreamt vpon two pretie things,
Hir thoughts they were affections chiefest neasts:
She suckt and sightht, and bathde hir in the springs,
And when she wakt they were my Mistres breasts.

Once Cupide sought a holde to couch his kisses,
And found the bodie of my best beloude.
Wherein he closde the beautie of his blisses,
And from that bower can neuer be remoude.

The Graces earst, when Alcidelian *springs*
Were waxen drie, perhaps did finde hir fountaine
Within the vale of blisse, where Cupides *wings*
Doo shield the Nectar fleeting from the mountaine.

No more fond man: things infinite I see
Brooke no dimension: Hell a foolish speech;
For endles things may neuer talked be.
Then let me liue to honor and beseech.

Sweete Natures pompe, if my deficient phraze
Hath staind thy glories by too little skill,
Yeeld pardon though mine eye that long did gaze,
Hath left no better pattern to my quill.

I will no more, no more will I detaine
Your listning eares with dallyance of my tongue:
I speake my ioyes, but yet conceale my paine;
My paine too olde, although my yeers be yong.

As soone as *Melicertus* had ended this Eclogue, they
expected the doome of *Democles*, who hearing the
sweete description, wherein *Melicertus* described his
Mistres, wondered that such rare conceipts could bee
harboured vnder a shepheards gray cloathing, at last he
made this aunswere.

Arcadian Swaines, whose wealth is content, whose
labours are tempred with sweete loues, whose mindes
aspyre not, whose thoughts brooke no enuie; onely as
riualls in affection, you are friendly emulators in honest
fancie: sith fortune (as enemie to your quiet) hath reft
you of your fayre shepheardesse, (the worlds wonder,
and *Arcadies* miracle) and one of you as champion must

lead the rest to reuenge, both desirous to shew your valour as your forwardnesse in affections, and yet (as I said) one to be sole chieftaine of the traine, I award to *Melicertus* that honor (as to him that hath most curiously portrayed out his Mistres excellencie) to beare the sole rule and supremacie. At this *Menaphon* grudged, and *Melicertus* was in an extasie for ioy; so that gathering all his forces together of stout headstrong clownes, amounting to the number of some two hundred, he apparailed himselfe in armour, colour sables, as mourning for his Mistres, in his shield he had figured the waues of the sea, *Venus* sitting on them in the height of all her pride. Thus marched *Melicertus* forward with olde *Democles* the supposed shepheard till they came to the castle, where *Pleusidippus* and his faire *Samela* were resident. As soone as they came there, *Melicertus* begirt the Castle with such a siege, as so manie sheepish Caualiers could furnish: which when he had done, summoning them in the Castle to parley, the yong Knight stept vpon the walls, and seeing such a crue of base companions, with Iackets and rustie bills on their backs, fell into a great laughter, and began to taunt them thus.

Why, what straunge Metamorphosis is this? Are the Plaines of *Arcadie*, whilome filled with labourers, now ouerlaide with launces? Are sheepe transformed into men, swaines into souldiers, and a wandring companie of poore shepheards, into a worthie troope of resolute champions? No doubt, either *Pan* meanes to playe the God of warre, or else these be but such men as rose of the teeth of *Cadmus*. Nowe I see the beginning of your warres, and the pretended ende of your stratagems: the shepheards haue a madding humor like the *Greekes* to seek for the recouerie of *Helena*; so you for the regain-

ing of your faire *Samela*. Heere she is Shepheards, and
I a *Priam* to defende hir with resistance of a ten yeares
siege; yet for I were loath to haue my Castle sackte like
Troy, I pray you tell me which is *Agamemnon?*

Melicertus hearing the youth speake thus proudly,
hauing the sparkes of honor fresh vnder the cinders of
pouertie, incited with loue and valor (two things to animate the most dastard *Thersites* to enter combate against
Hercules) answered thus.

Vnknowen yongster of *Thessaly*, if the feare of thy
hardie deedes, were like the Diapason of thy threates,
wee woulde thinke the Castle of longer siege, than
either our ages would permit, or our valour aduenture:
but where the shelfe is most shallowe, there the water
breakes most high; emptie vessells haue the highest
sounds, hollowe rockes the loudest ecchoes, and pratling gloriosers, the smallest performaunce of courage;
for proofe whereof, seeing thou hast made a rape of
faire *Samela*, one of her vowed Shepheards is come
for the safetie of hir sweete selfe to challenge thee to
single combat; if thou ouercome me, thou shalt freelie
passe with the shepheardesse to *Thessaly*; if I vanquish
thee, thou shalt feele the burthen of thy rashnesse, and
Samela the sweetnesse of her libertie. *Pleusidippus* mer-
uailed at the resolution of the shepheard ; but when
Democles heard how if hee wonne, she should be transported into *Thessaly*, a world of sorowes tombled in his
discontented braine, that he hammered in his head
many meanes to stay the faire *Samela*; for when *Pleusidippus* in a great choller was readie to throwe downe
his gantlet, and to accept of the combat, *Democles* step-
ped vp and spoke thus: Worthie mirrors of resolued
magnanimitie, whose thoughts are aboue your fortunes,

and whose valour more than your reuenewes, knowe
that Bitches that puppie in haſt bring foorth blind
whelpes; that there is no herbe sooner sprong vp than
the Spattarmia, nor sooner fadeth; that fruits too soone
ripe are quickly rotten; that deedes done in haſt are
repented at leisure: then braue men, in so weightie a
cause, and for the conqueſt of so excellent a Paragon,
let not one minute begin and end the quarrell, but like
Fabius of *Rome* vse delay in such dangerous exploytes,
when honor sits on wreaths of Lawrell to giue the victor his garland: deferre it some three daies, and then in
solemne manner end the combat. To this good motion
not onely *Pleusidippus* and *Melicertus* agreed, but all the
companie were consenting, and vpon pledges of truce
being giuen, they reſted. But *Democles* seeing in couerte
he could not conquer, and that in despairing loues, secrecie was no salue, he dispatched letters to the Nobilitie of his court, with ſtraight charge that they should
bee in that place within three dayes with tenne thousand
ſtrong. This newes no sooner came to the Generall of
his Forces, but leuying so many approoued souldiers, he
marched secretly by night to the place *Democles* in his
letters had prescribed; and there ioyfully interteined by
the King, they were placde in ambush readie when the
signall should be giuen to issue out of the place, and
performe their Souereignes command. Well, the third
day being come, no sooner did Titan arise from the
watrie Couche of his Lemman, but these two champions were readie in the liſtes, accompanied with the
route of all the *Arcadian* shepheards, and olde *Democles*
whom they had appoynted for one of the Iudges. *Pleusidippus* seeing *Melicertus* aduãce on his shield the
waues of the sea with a *Venus* sitting vppon them, mer-

H

uailed what the shepheard should be that gaue his
armes, and *Melicertus* was as much amazed to see a
strange *Thessalian* Knight vant his armes without difference; yet being so fraught with direfull reuenge, as
they scorned to salute each other so much as with
threates, they fell toughly to blowes. *Samela* standing
on top of the turret, and viewing the combate; the poore
Ladie grieuing that for her cause such a stratageme
should arise in *Arcadie*, her countenance ful of sorrow,
and flouds of teares falling from her eyes, she began to
breath out this passion.

Vnfortunate *Samela* born to mishaps, and forepoint-
ed to sinister fortunes, whose bloomes were ripened by
mischance, and whose fruite is like to wither with despaire; in thy youth sate discontent pruning her selfe on
thy forhead, now in thine age sorrow hides her selfe
amongst the wrinckles of thy face: thus art thou infortunate in thy Prime, and crossed with cõtrarie accidents
in thy Autumne; as haplesse as *Helena* to haue the
burden of warres laid on the wings of thy beautie. And
who must be the champion? whose sword must pearce
the helme of thine enemie? whose bloud must purchase
the freedome of *Samela*, but *Melicertus*? If he conquer,
then *Samela* triumphs, as if she had been chiefe victor
in the *Olympiades*; if he loose, euerie drop falling from
his wounds into the center of my thoughts, as his death
to him, so shall it be to me the ende of my loues, my
life, and my libertie. As still shee was about to goe forwarde in hir passion, the trumpet sounded and they fell
to fight in such furious sorte, as the *Arcadians* and
Democles himselfe wondered to see the courage of the
Shepheard, that tied the Knight to such a sore taske.
Pleusidippus likewise feeling an extraordinarie kinde of

force, and seeing with what courage the Knight of the shepheards fought, beganne to coniecture diuersly of the waues, and to feare the euent of the combate. On the contrarie parte, *Melicertus* halfe wearied with the heauie blowes of *Pleusidippus*, ſtoode in a maze howe so yong a wagge should be so expert in his weapon. Thus debating diuersly in their seueral thoughts, at length being both wearie, they ſtepte backe, and leaning on their swordes tooke breath, gazing each vpon other. At laſt *Pleusidippus* burſt into these speaches.

Shepheard in life, though now a Gentleman in armour, if thy degree be better, I glorie I am not disgracde with the combate: tell me, how dareſt thou so farre wrong mee, as to weare mine Armes vpon thy shield?

Princockes (quoth *Melicertus*) thou lieſt, they bee mine owne, and thou contrarie to the Lawe of Armes beareſt my Creaſt without difference, in which quarrell, seeing it concernes mine honour, I will reuenge it as farre as my loues; and with that he gaue such a charging blowe at *Pleusidippus* healme, that hee had almoſt ouerturned him: *Pleusidippus* lefte not the blowe vnrequitted, but doubled his force; insomuch that the hazard of the battaile was doubtfull, and both of them were faine to take breath againe. *Democles* seeing his time, that both of them were sore weakened, gaue the watchword, and the ambush leapt out, slaughtered manie of the shepheards, put the reſt to flight, tooke the two champions prisoners, and sacking the Caſtle, carried them and the faire *Samela* to his Court: letting the Shepheardesse haue her libertie, but putting *Melicertus* and *Pleusidippus* into a deepe and darke dungeon.

Where leauing these passionate Louers in this *Cata-*

strophe, againe to *Doron* the homely blunt Shephearde; who hauing been long enamoured of *Carmela*, much good wooing past betwixte them, and yet little speeding; at last, both of them met hard by the Promontorie of *Arcadie*, shee leading foorth her Sheepe, and hee going to see his newe yeand Lambes. As soone as they met, breaking a few quarter blowes with such countrey glaunces as they coulde, they geerde one at another louingly. At last *Doron* manfully begun thus.

Carmela by my troth God morrow, tis as daintie to see you abroad, as to eate a messe of sweete milke in Iuly: you are proude such a house doue of late, or rather so good a Huswife, that no man may see you vnder a couple of Capons; the Church-yeard may stand long inough ere you will come to looke on it, and the Piper may begge for euerie pennie he gets out of your pursse: but it is no matter, you are in loue with some stout Ruffler, and yet poore folkes, such a I am, must be content with porredge: and with that, turning his backe, he smiled in his sleeue to see howe kindely hee had giuen her the bobbe: which *Carmela* seeing, she thought to be euen with him thus.

Indeede *Doron* you saye well, it is long since wee met, and our house is a Grange house with you: but we haue tyed vp the great Dogge, and when you come you shall haue greene rushes you are such a straunger: but tis no matter; soone hot soone colde, hee that mingles himselfe with drasse, the hogges will eate him: and she that layes her loue on an vnkinde man, shall finde sorrowe inough to eate hir soppes withall. And with that *Carmela* was so full stomackt that she wept.

Doron to shewe himselfe a naturall young man, gaue her a few kinde kisses to comfort her, and sware that she

was the woman he loued best in the whole worlde, and
for proofe quoth he, thou shalt heare what I will praise:
and you quoth she, what I will performe. And so taking
hand in hand, they kindly sate them downe, and began
to discourse their loues in these Eclogues.

Dorons Eclogue ioynd
with Carmelas.

Sit downe Carmela *here are cubbs for kings,*
Slowes blacke as ieat, or like my Christmas shooes,
Sweete Sidar which my leathren bottle brings:
Sit downe Carmela *let me kisse thy toes.*

Carmela.

Ah Doron, *ah my heart, thou art as white,*
As is my mothers Calfe or brinded Cow,
Thine eyes are like the slow wormes in the night,
Thine haires resemble thickest of the snow.

The lines within thy face are deepe and cleere
Like to the furrowes of my fathers waine,
Thy sweate vpon thy face dooth oft appeare
Like to my mothers fat and Kitchin gaine.

Ah leaue my toe and kisse my lippes my loue,
My lippes and thine, for I haue giuen it thee:
Within thy cap tis thou shalt weare my gloue,
At foote ball sport thou shalt my champion be.

Doron.

Carmela *deare, euen as the golden ball*
That Venus *got, such are thy goodly eyes,*
When cherries iuice is iumbled therewithall,
Thy breath is like the steeme of apple pies.

Thy lippes resemble two Cowcumbers faire,
Thy teeth like to the tuskes of fattest swine,
Thy speach is like the thunder in the aire:
Would God thy toes, thy lips and all were mine.

Carmela.

Doron *what thing dooth mooue this wishing griefe.*

Doron.

Tis Loue Carmela *ah tis cruell Loue.*
That like a slaue, and caitiffe villaine thiefe,
Hath cut my throate of ioy for thy behoue.

Carmela.

Where was he borne?

Doron.

In faith I know not where.
But I haue had much talking of his dart.
Ay me poore man, with manie a trampling teare,
I feele him wound the forehearse of my heart,

What doo I loue? O no, I doo but talke.
What shall I die for loue? O no, not so.
What am I dead? O no my tongue dooth walke.
Come kisse Carmela, *and confound my woe.*

Carmela.

Euen with this kisse, as once my father did,
I seale the sweete indentures of delight:
Before I breake my vowe the Gods forbid,
No not by day, nor yet by darkesome night.

Doron.

Euen with this garland made of Holly-hocks
I crosse thy browes from euerie shepheards kisse.
Heigh hoe how glad am I to touch thy lockes,
My frolicke heart euen now a free man is,

Carmela.

I thanke you Doron, *and will thinke on you,*
I loue you Doron, *and will winke on you.*
I seale your charter pattent with my thummes,
Come kisse and part for feare my mother comes.

Thus ended this merrie Eclogue betwixte *Doron* and *Carmela*: which Gentlemen if it be stufft with pretie Similes and farre fetcht Metaphores; thinke the poore Countrey Louers knewe no further comparisons, than came within compasse of their Countrey Logicke. Well, twas a good worlde when such simplicitie was vsed, sayes the olde women of our time, when a ring of a rush woulde tye as much Loue together as a Gimmon of golde: but Gentlemen since wee haue talkte of Loue so long, you shall giue me leaue to shewe my opinion of that foolish fancie thus.

Sonetto.

What thing is Loue? It is a power diuine
That raines in vs: or else a wreakefull law
That doomes our mindes to beautie to encline:
It is a starre whose influence dooth draw
    Our hearts to Loue dissembling of his might,
    Till he be master of our hearts and sight.
Loue is a discord and a strange diuorce
Betwixt our sense and reason, by whose power
As madde with reason we admit that force,
Which wit or labour, neuer may deuoure,
    It is a will that brooketh no consent:
    It would refuse, yet neuer may repent.
Loue's a desire, which for to waite a time,
Dooth loose an age of yeeres, and so doth passe
As dooth the shadow seuerd from his prime,
Seeming as though it were, yet neuer was.
    Leauing behinde nought but repentant thoughts
    Of daies ill spent, for that which profits noughts.
Its now a peace, and then a sodaine warre,
A hope consumde before it is conceiude,
At hand it feares, and menaceth a farre,
And he that gaines is most of all deceiude:
    It is a secret hidden and not knowne,
    Which one may better feele than write vpon.

Thus Gentlemen haue you heard my verdite in this *Sonetto*, now will I returne to *Doron* and *Carmela*, who not seeing her mother come, fell againe to a few homely kisses, and thus it was.

After they had thus amorously ended their Eclogues, they plighted faith and troth; and *Carmela* verie brisk-

lye wiping her mouth with a white apron sealed it with a
kisse, which *Doron* taking merueilous kindly, after a
little playing loath to depart, they both went about their
businesse. Leauing them therefore to their businesse,
again to *Democles;* who seeing no intreaties would serue
to perswade *Samela* to loue, neither the hope of the
Arcadian Crowne, nor the title of a Queene, laſtly as-
sayed with frownes and threates, but all in vaine: for
Samela firſt reſtrained by nature in that he was her
Father, and secondly by loue in that *Melicertus* lay imprisoned onely for her sake, ſtoode ſtill so ſtiffe to her
tackling, that *Democles* chaunging loue into hate, resolued to reuenge that with death, which no meanes els
might satisfie: so that to colour his frauds withall, he
gaue *Samela* free license to visite *Melicertus*: which she
had not long done, but that by the inſtigation of the old
King, the gailor confederate to his treacherie, accuseth
her of adulterie: wherevpon without further witnesse
they both were condemned to dye. These two louers
knowing themselues guiltlesse in this surmised faction,
were ioyfull to ende their loues with their liues, and so
to conclude all in a fatall and finall content of mindes
and passions. But *Democles* set free *Pleusidippus,* as
afraide the King of *Thessaly* would reuenge the wrong
of his Knight, intertaining him with sumptuous banquets, as befitted so braue and worthie a Gentleman.
The day came prefixed wherein these parties should
die; *Samela* was so desirous to end her life with her
friend, that she would not reueale either vnto *Democles*
or *Melicertus* what she was; and *Melicertus* rather chose
to die with his *Samela,* than once to name himself *Maximius.* Both thus resolued, were brought to the place of
execution; and *Pleusidippus* sitting on a scaffolde with

Democles, seeing *Samela* come forth like the blush of the morning, felt an vncouth passion in his mind, and nature began to enter combate with his thoughtes; not loue but reuerence, not fancie but feare began to assaile him, that he turnd to the King, and sayd: Is it not pitie *Democles*, such diuine beautie should be wrapt in cinders: No quoth *Democles*, where the anger of a King must be satisfied. At this answere *Pleusidippus* wrapt his face in his cloake and wept, and all the assistants grieued to see so faire a creature subiect to the violent rage of fortune. Well *Democles* commaunded the deathsman to doo his deuoyre; who kneeling downe and crauing pardon, readie to giue *Melicertus* the fatall stroake, there stept out an olde woman attired like a Prophetesse, who cried out; Villaine hold thy hand, thou wrongest the daughter of a King. *Democles* hearing the outcrie, and seeing that at that word the people begun to mutinie and murmur, demanded the olde woman what she meant? Now quoth she, *Democles* is the *Delphian* oracle performed; *Neptune* hath yeelded vp the worlds wonder, and that is young *Pleusidippus* nephew to thee, and sonne to faire *Sephestia*, who heere standeth vnder the name of *Samela*, cast vpon the Promontorie of *Arcadie* with her yong sonne, where shee as a shepheardesse hath liude in labours tempred with loues; her son playing on the shore, was conveyed by certaine Pirates into *Thessaly*, where (when as he was supposed euerie waye to be dead) doing deedes of chiualrie, he fulfilled the prophecie: your highnesse giuing the Lyon, were guid vnto the lambs in dissembling your selfe a shepheard: planets resting vpon the hills, was the picture of *Venus* vpon their crests: and the seas that had neither ebbe nor tide, was the combate twixte the father

and the sonne, that gaue the waues of the seas in their
shields, not able to vanquish one another, but parting
with equall victorie. For know *Democles* this *Melicertus*
is *Maximius*, twice betrothed to *Sepheſtia*, and Father to
yong *Pleusidippus*: nowe therefore the Oracle fulfilled,
is the happie time wherein *Arcadie* shal reſt in peace.
At this, the people gaue a great shout, and the olde
woman vanisht. *Democles* as a man rauisht with an
extasie of sodaine ioye, sate ſtill, and ſtared on the face
of *Sepheſtia*: *Pleusidippus* in all dutie leapt from his
seate, and went and couered his mother with his roabe,
crauing pardon for the fondnesse of his inceſtuous affection: and kneeling at his fathers feete submisse in
that he had drawen his sword, and sought his life that
first in this world gaue him life. *Maximius* firſt looked
on his wife, and seeing by the lineaments of her face
that it was *Sepheſtia*, fell about her necke, and both of
them weping in the bosome of their sonne shed teares
for ioye to see him so braue a Gentleman. *Democles* all
this while sitting in a trance, at laſt calling his senses
together, seeing his daughter reuiued, whom so cruelly
for the loue of *Maximius* he had banisht out his confines, *Maximius* in safetie, and the childe a matchles
paragon of approued chiualrie, he leapt from his seate,
and imbraced them all with teares, crauing pardon of
Maximius and *Sepheſtia*: and to shew that the outward
obiect of his watrie eies, had a sympathie with the inward passion of his hart, he impald the head of his yong
neuew *Pleusidippus* with the crowne and diadem of *Arcadie*: and for that his brother *Lamedon* had in all distresse not lefte his daughter *Sepheſtia*, he toke the matter so kindly, that he reconciled himselfe vnto him, and
made him Duke in *Arcady*. The successe of this forere-

hearsed Cataſtrophe growing so comicall, they all concluded after the Feſtiuall solemnizing of the Coronation
(which was made famous with the excellent deedes of
manie worthie Caualiers) to passe into *Thessaly*, to contract the mariage twixt *Pleusidippus*, and the daughter
of the *Thessalian* King. Which newes spred thorough
Arcadie as a wonder, that at laſt it came to *Menaphons*
eares; who hearing the high parentage of his supposed
Samela, seeing his passions were too aspiring, and that
with the *Syrian* wolues he barkt againſt the Moone, he
lefte such lettice as were too fine for his lips, and courted
his old loue *Pesana*, to whom shortly after he was married. And leſt there should be left any thing vnperfect
in this paſtorall accident, *Doron* smudgde himselfe vp,
and iumpde a marriage with his old friend *Carmela*.

FINIS.

A Margarite of America

By T. Lodge

Printed for *Iohn Busbie*, and are to be
sold in S. Dunstons church-yard in
Fleet-street, at the little shop
next Cliffords Inne.
1595

To the noble, learned and vertuous Ladie,
the Ladie Russell, *T.L. wisheth affluence*
on earth, and felicitie in heauen.

MADAM, your deep and considerate iudgement your admired honor and happy readings haue drawne me to present this labor of mine to your gracious hands, and fauorable patronage: wherein, though you shall find nothing to admire; yet doubt I not but you may meet many things that deserue cherishing. Touching the subiect, though of it selfe it seeme historicall yet if it please you like our English *Sapho*, to look into that which I haue slenderly written, I doubt not but that your memory shal acquaint you with my diligence, and my diligence may deserue your applause. Touching the place where I wrote this, it was in those straits christned by *Magelan*; in which place to the southward many wonderous Isles, many strange fishes, many monstrous Patagõnes withdrew my senses; briefly, many bitter and extreme frosts at midsummer continually clothe and clad the discomfortable mountaines; so that as there was great wonder in the place wherein I writ this, so likewise might it be maruelled, that in such scantie fare, such causes of feare, so mightie discouragements, and many crosses, I should deserue or eternize anything. Yet what I haue done (good Madame) iudge and hope this felicitie from my pen, that whilst the memorie thereof shal liue in any age, your charitie,

learning, nobilitie and vertues shall be eternized. *Op
pian* writing to *Theodosius* was as famous by the person
to whome hee consecrated his study, as fortunate in his
labours, which as yet are not mastered by obliuion; so
hope I (Madame) on the wing of your sacred name to
be borne to the temple of Eternitie, where though enuie
barke at me the Muses shall cherish, loue, and happie
me. Thus hoping your Ladiship will supply my bold
nesse with your bountie and affabilitie, I humbly kisse
your most delicate handes, shutting vp my English
duety vnder an Italian copie of humanitie and curtesie
From my house this 4. of Maie 1596.

Your Honors in all zeale,

T . L O D G E .

¶ *To the Gentlemen Readers.*

GENTLEMEN, I am preuented in mine own hopes; in seconding thrifts forward desires. Som foure yeres since being at sea with *M. Candish* (whose memorie if I repent not, I lament not) it was my chance in the librarie of the Iesuits in *Sanctum* to find this historie in the Spanish tong, which as I read delighted me, and delighting me, wonne me, and winning me, made me write it. The place where I began my worke, was a ship, where many souldiers of good reckning finding disturbed stomackes; it can not but stand with your discretions to pardon an vndiscreete and vnstaied penne, for hands may vary where stomacks miscary. The time I wrote in, was when I had rather will to get my dinner, then to win my fame. The order I wrote in, was past order, where I rather obserued mens hãds lest they should strike me, then curious reason of men to condemne mee. In a worde, I wrote vnder hope rather the fish should eate both me writing, and my paper written, then fame should know me, hope should acquaint her with me, or any but miserie should heare mine ending. For those faults (gentlemen) escaped by the Printer, in not being acquainted with my hand, and the booke printed in my absence, I must craue you with fauour to iudge of, and with your wonted curtesies to correct; and according to Ecclesiastcall law, giue vs on our confession absolution: if you will not, remember this, that a countrie lasse for Ladies, may tell them they curle too much; and for Gentlemen, that they are vnfashioned by

I

their fashions. To be short, who liues in this world, let him wincke in the world; for either men prooue too blinde in seeing too litle, or too presumptuous in condemning
that they shoulde not.

Yours T. Lodge.

¶A Margarite of America

For Ladies Delight, and Ladies Honour

THE blushing morning gan no sooner appeare from the desired bed of her old paramor, and remembring air of hir *Cephalus*, watered the bosome of sweete floures with the christal of hir teares: but both the armies (awaked by the harmonie of the birds, that recorded their melody in euery bush, began to arme them n their tents, and speedily visit their trenches: Among the rest the two emperors (the one, *Protomachus* of *Mosco*, the other, *Artosogon* of *Cusco*) considering with themselues, the care Princes ought to haue that command multitudes; the prefixed houre of their fight already arriued, sodainely armed themselues, commanding their corronels by sound of trumpet to draw out their companies into the plain: Then marched forth ech squadron, deaffing the aire with their cries, dimming the sunne with the reflexion of their costly curets, their high lookes promised happy forwardnes, and their haughtie hearts were portraied in their dreadlesse demeane. At the last embattailed in due order, the pikemen in a *Macedonian* phalanx, the horsemen in their out-wings, the shot as gards to the pikes, al as protectors of their colours, the fatall charge was sounded, and both the armies marched forward to incounter: (when sodainly an old man, whose sober lookes betokened his seuere thoughts, whose morneful garments, shadowed, his melancholie minde,) bearing the Image of the Gods, whom he most honoured) betweene his armes, and the homage a true subiect ought to haue in his heart, thrust himselfe betweene both the armies, when sending many sighes from his breast to famous pittie, and teares from his eies to moue compassion, he fixed both his hands on their knees (who were neerely encountered to enter combate) and began in their termes to perswade both the monarchs (whilst both the armies withdrew their weapons, to giue diligent attention to his words:) Stay your vnbridled furies, O you Princes, and let not the world say, that you who were borne to be the defenders of the monarchies, are (through your il-gouerned furies) become the destroyers of mankinde. Whereto tendeth this your vniust armes? if for your priuate grudges; oh how fond are you, that to reuenge your mislikes, are the murtherers of many innocents? If to enlarge your signiories; oh how vaine are you, that seek to attaine that with bloud, which you must keepe with care; that labor to sell that with stripes, which you haue bought with peace; that trauel to loose your own estates and signiories, for alitle name of souerainty? Heare me O you Princes (nay rather be aduised by me:) you haue spent huge treasures, made many widdowes, lost three yeares, and for what I pray you? for the right of one citie, the whole confines and reuenewes whereof is not sufficient to acquit for one moneth of your charges: O vnhappy *Mantinea*, the cause of such hartburning: O lawles name of seigniory, the occasion of such sorrows. Heare what *Plutarch* saith, Ye potentates, there is no warre that taketh head amongst men, but of vice: for either the loue of pleasure, either couetousnes, ambition or desire of rule, prouoketh the same. If this be true, as it is most certaine, why blush you not (Princes) to behold your owne follies? why reconcile you not to amend your misdeedes? If you say there are more pleasures in *Man-tinea*, then in your seuerall countries, you detract from whole prouinces, to make proud one poore cittie: and if it were, what a vaine thing is it, that such as are in authority should purchase a priuate delight by publike danger? *Plato* being demanded why he praised the *Lydians* so much, and dispraised the *Lacedemonians* so highly, answered thus: If I commend the *Lydians*, it is for that they were neuer occupied but in tilling the field: and if I do reproue the *Lacedemonians*, it is because they knew nothing else but to conquer Realmes: so vertuous a thing hath it bin held by the learned to maintaine peace, and to shunne occasions of contention. If you will be held vertuous and monarchies (as I wish you should be) desire nothing to the domage of your com-mon weales, leſt in satisfying your owne humors ye subuert your subiects happines. If for couetousnes ye hunt after conqueſts, how vaine are you, labouring like mad men to lay more ſtraw on your houses to burn them, and caſt more water on the sea to drowne it? Couetousnes is an affection that hath no end, an ex-treame that hath no meane, a profit full of preiudice. Wel said *Ariſtotle* in his Politikes, there is no extreme pouertie but that of couetousnes. If for ambitiõ, wel may ye weep with *Alexander*, to be laughed at, practise with *Zenos*, to repent with him: for in desiring beyond your reach, you fall besides your hopes. But if all these euills be growen to one head, if your incontinencie in desire, your excessiue thirſt after pleasure, your couet-ous longing after riches, your ambitious hunting after seignioritie, haue occasioned this warre; subdue these errors in your selues for your subiects sakes: and sith *Protomachus* hath one daughter, and no more to inherit

Mosco, and *Artosogon* one sonne and heire to suceede in
the Empire of *Cusco*, let both these be ioyned together
in happie matrimonie: so shall the cause of this different
be quicklie decided, your selfe may roote out your ingrafted errors, your subiects enioy their desired peace,
and finally, your Children shal haue greater cause to
praise their fathers foresight, then to repent hereafter
their vniuſt furie. Hereunto I coniure you, O you
Princes, by these holy gods, whom you honour, by
these hoarie haires which you should reuerence, leſt
your subiects hereafter ruinated through your rashnes,
haue rather occasion to curse you then commend you.
In *Octauius Cæsars* time, each one thought himselfe fortunate to be borne vnder his emperie, and him happie
that maintained his prouince in peace: so let it be said
of you (good Princes) and leaue you such memorie to
your succession: then shall I thinke my selfe happie in
my perswasions, and you shall be famous to all poſter-
itie.

No sooner had he ended his oration, but both the
emperors resolued, by his reasons, and pacified by the
perswasions of their nobilitie (who after long debate
and consultation, and cheare behoouefull) drew to an
accord: wherein it was concluded, that *Arsadachus* the
youthful heire of *Cusco* shoulde bee sent to the emperor
of *Mosco*, where, (considering the worthines of his court)
he shuld find fit companions, and apply himself to fancie,
being continually in the presence of his faire *Margarita*:
finally (after the decease of both the Princes) it was
enacted that both *Mantinea* and the whole empire,
should remaine to *Arsadachus*, and *Margarita* and their
heires for euer. These articles thus concluded vpon,
both the campes brake up; the braue knights who to-

fore time delighted in tossing of lances, now haue no other pleasure but in talking with faire Ladies, the souldiers sword, was changed to a husbandmans sithe; his gay Curets, to a grey frocke; the gates which before-time were shut against foes, were now opened to all sorts as vnsuspected friends: Such libertie followeth peace, exempted from the tyranny of warre. *Artosogon* withdrew his folowers to his owne frontires, and return-ing to his court, made honourable prouision for his sonne *Arsadachus* to send him to *Moscouia*. *Protomachus* (after he had rewarded each souldier according to his desert) withdrew himselfe to the castel of that aged father, who had so faithfully councelled him, (yeelding him for rewarde the dukedome of *Volgradia*, the chiefest place of honor through all *Moscouy*) whither, as to the open theater of al delights, the nobility and ladies resort-ed, among the which the chiefest, fairest, and chastest *Margarita*, presented her selfe, reioycing at the happie reconcilement: where being resolued by hir father of ye contract that was concluded upon, with blushes at first shewed hir modestie, and with obedience at last con-descended to his minde. In this rare fortresse of *Arsin-ous* (scituate by a gratious and siluer floting riuer, in-uironed with curious planted trees to minister shade, and sweete smelling floures, to recreate the sences; be-sides the curious knots, the daintie gardin plots, the rich tapestrie, the royall attendance) *Protomachus* found as euident signes of high spirit, as of huge expence: at the entrance, of his chamber (which had a prospect into a delicious garden in which al sorts of birds inclosed in a Cage of christall recorded their harmonies, whilst the gentle fall of a bubling fountaine seemed to yeeld a sweet and murmuring consent to their musicke) was placed that sentence of *Drusius Germanicus* which he carried alwayes ingraued in his ring.

Illis est grauis fortuna quibus est repentina.

About the walles of the chamber in curious imagerie were the seuen sages of Greece, set forth with their seueral vertues, eloquently discouered in *Arabicke* verses: The bed appointed for the prince to rest himselfe, was of blacke Ebonie enchased with Rubies, Diamons and Carbuncls, made in form of an arch, on which by degrees mans state from infancie to his olde age was plainly depictured, and on the testerne of the bed the whole contents of the same most sagelie deciphered in these verses.

Humanæ Miseriæ discursus.

O whereof boasteth man, or by what reason
Is filthy clay so much ambitious?
Whose thoughts are vaine, and alter euery season,
Whose deedes are damned, base, and vitious,
Who in his cradle by his childish crying
Presageth his mishaps and sorrowes nying.

An infant first from nurces teat he sucketh
With nutriment corruption of his nature:
And from the roote of endlesse errour plucketh
That taste of sinne that waites on euery creature,
And as his sinewes firme his sinne increaseth,
And but till death his sorrow neuer ceaseth.

In riper yeares when youthly courage raineth,
A winters blast of fortunes lowring changes,

A flattering hope wherein no trust remaineth,
A fleeting loue his forward ioy estranges:
Atchiue he wealth, with wastefull wo he bought it,
Let substance faile, he grieues, and yet he sought it.

In staied yeares when as he seekes the gleanings
Of those his times in studious Artes bestowed,
In summe, he oft misconstrueth wise-mens meanings,
Soiling the spring from whence his science flowed,
In all he gaines by perfect iudgement gained,
A hate of life that hath so long remained.

From height of throne to abiect wretchednesse,
From woonderous skill to seruile ignorance:
From court to cart, from rich to rechlesnesse,
The ioyes of life haue no continuance:
The king, the caitife wretch, the lay, the learned,
Their crowns, woes, wants, and wits with griefe haue
*   erned.*

The Iudgement seate hath brawles, honour is hated,
The souldiers life is dayly thrall to danger,
The marchants bag by tempests is abated,
His stocke still serues for prey to euery stranger,
The scholler with his knowledge learnes repent,
Thus each estate in life hath discontent.

And in these trades and choice estates of liuing,
Youth steales on manly state, and it on age,
And age with weakned limmes, and mind misgiuing,
With trembling tongue repenteth youthly rage,
And ere he full hath learnd his life to gouerne,
He dies, and dying doth to dust returne.

His greatest good is, to report the trouble
Which he in prime of youth hath ouerpassed,
How for his graines of good he reapt but stubble,
How lost by loue, by follies hew disgraced,
Which whilst he counts, his sonne perhaps attendeth,
And yet his dayes in selfe like follies endeth.

Thus mortall life on sodaine vanisheth,
All like a dreame, or as the shadow fleeteth,
When sunne his beame from substance banisheth,
Or like the snow at once that dries and fleeteth,
Or as the rainebow which by her condition
Liues by the Sunnes reflect and opposition.

Thus life in name is but a death in beeing,
A burthen to the soule by earth intangled:
Then put thou off that vaile that lets thy seeing,
O wretched man with many torments mangled,
Since neither childe, nor youth, nor staid, nor aged,
The stormes of wretched life may be asswaged.

And with the Egyptian midst thy delicates
Present the shape of death in euery member,
To make thee know the name of all estates:
And midst thy pompe thy nying graue remember,
Which if thou dost, thy pride shall be repressed,
Since none before he dies is perfect blessed.

Thus sumptuous was the lodging of *Protomachus*, bu
far more glorious the chamber of *Margarita* whicl
seemed from the first day to be fashioned to her affec
tions, for ouer the entrance of the doores was drawer
and carued out of curious white marble, the faire god

desse of chaſtitie blushing at the sodaine interception of
Acteon, and her naked nymphes, who with the one hand,
couering their owne secret pleasures with blushes, with
the other caſt a beautifull vaile ouer their miſtresse
daintie nakednes: the two pillers of the doore were beau-
tified with the two *Cupids* of *Anacreon*, which well
shaped modeſtie often seemed to whip leſt they should
growe ouer wanton: no sooner was the inward beauties
of the chamber discouered, but the worke wrought his
wonder, and the wonder it selfe was equalled by the
worke, for al the chaſte Ladies of the world, inchased
out of siluer, looking through faire mirrours of chrisolites, carbuncles, saphires and greene Emeraults, fixed
their eies on the picture of eternitie, which fixed on the
toppes of a teſterne, seemed with a golden trumpet to
applaud to them al: in the tapiſtrie (beutified with gold,
and pearle) were the nine Muses curiously wrought,
who from a thicket beheld amorous *Orpheus* making
the trees leape through his laments, and as he warbled
his songs the flouds of *Hebrus* ſtaied their sources; and
the birds that beheld their comfort, began likewise to
carrol. It was ſtrange to thinke, and more ſtrange to
behold, in what order Art matched with nature, and
how the lymning painter had almoſt exceeded nature in
life, sauing that the beauteous faces wanted breath, to
make them aliue, not cunning to proue them liuely.
Thus was both the emperor and his daughter lodged,
wanting neither delights of hunting, nor other princely
plesures, to entertain them: so curious was the good
olde man, in pleasing his emperor and maſter. But
among al other courtly delights *Margarita* met not the
leaſt, who in this caſtle found a companion to accom-
panie hir in life, and a chaſte maide to attend her in

loue, who (beside hir education, which was excellent, hir virtues such as equalled excellence, hir beuty so rare as exceeded both) was beloued by a noble lord of *Moscouy*, who for his singularities in poetry, and science in feats of arms, was rather the seignior, then second of al the empire. The enterchange of which affections was so conformable to the fancies of the princesse, that she, who was ordained to be the miracle of loue, learnd by them and their maners the true methode of the same: for when *Minecius* courted his *Philenia*, *Margarita* conceited her *Arsadachus*; and by perceiuing the true heart of the one, supposed the perfect habite of the other. If at any time cause of discourtesie grew betwixt *Philenia* and her friend, *Margarita* salued it, hoping by that means to sacrifice to Loue, to gratifie him in her fortunes, which were to succeede. How often would she make *Minecius* deserts excellent by her praise, and he his *Philenia* famous by his poetrie? It was a world to see in them, that when loue waxed warm, those louers waxed wittie, the one to command, the other to consent: if at any time *Minecius* wrote an amorous sonnet, *Margarita* should see it: and if at any time *Margarita* read a sonet she would commend it to satisfie *Philenia*, and in that *Arsinous* (the father through the good opinion of *Protomachus* the Emperour, thought not amisse of the marriage betweene his daughter and the *Moscouite*,) he rather furthered then frouned on their paſtimes: and *Minecius* hauing achiued her father and intangled the daughter in fancie, sought all meanes possible to satisfie her delights; sometimes therefore under a paſtorall habite he would hide him in the groues and woods where the Ladies were accuſtomed to walke, where recording a ruthful lay as they passed by; hee through his

harmonie, caused them beleeue that the tree tattled
loue, and such was his method in his melancholy fancies, that his coate was accordant to his conceit, and his
conceit the miracle of conceits: among the rest these of
no small regard, I haue thought good in this place to
register, which though but few in number are worthie
the noting. First being on a time melancholy by reson
of some mislikes of his mistris he wrote these sonets, in
imitation of *Dolce* the Italian, and presented them in
presence of the Princes *Margarita*, who highly commended them, ouer the top whereof he wrote this in
great Roman letters.

PIETATI.

If so those flames I vent when as I sigh,
Amidst these lowly vallies where I lie,
Might finde some meanes by swift addresse to flie
Vnto those Alpine toplesse mountaines high:

Thou shouldst behold their Icie burthens thawe,
And crimson flowers adorne their naked backs,
Sweete roses should inrich their winter wracks,
Against the course of kind and natures lawe.

But you faire Ladie see the furious flame,
That through your will destroyes me beyond measure,
Yet in my paines me thinkes you take great pleasure,
Loth to redeeme or else redresse the fame:
    Nor hath your heart compassion of mine illes,
    More cold then snow, more hard then Alpine hils.

The other was this which seemed to be written with
more vehemencie of spirit, and farre greater melan-

cholie, which in a shepheards habite, sitting vnder a Mirtle tree he had mornfully recorded in the presence of his miſtresse.

PIETATI.

O desarts be you peopled by my plaints,
And let your plantes by my pure teares be watred,
And let the birds whom my sad mone acquaint,
To heare my hymnes haue harmonie in hatred.

Let all your sauage citizens refraine,
To haunt those bowers where I my woes bewray,
Let none but deepe dispaire with me remaine,
To haſte my death when hope doth will me ſtay.

Let rocks remoue for feare they melt to heare me,
Let Eccho whiſt for dread shee die to answere:
So liuing thus where no delights come neere me,
My manie mones more moouing may appeare:
　　And in the depth of all when I am climing,
　　Let loue come by, see, sigh, and fall a crying.

This mourning passion pleased the ladies very highly, especially *Philenia*, who thought her selfe no little blessed to bee thus beloued: among the reſt they gaue this that follows his deserued commendation; for being written in the desolate season of the yeare, and the desperate successe of his earnings, being so applied to his affects, and accordant with the yeares effects, (in my minde) deserueth no small good liking.

With Ganimede now ioines the shining sunne,
And through the world displaise his chiller flame,

Cold, frost, and snow, the meddowes, and the mountaines
Do wholie blend, the waters waxen Ice:
The meades want flowers, the trees haue parched leaues,
Such is the dolie season of the yeare.

And I in coldest season of the yeare,
Like to a naked man before the Sunne,
Whilest drought thus dwels in herbes and dried leaues,
Consume my selfe, and in affections flame
To cinders fall: ne helpes me frost or ice
That falles from off these Snow-clad cloudie mountains.

But when as shades new clothe againe the mountaines,
And daies wax long, and warmer is the yeare,
Then in my soule fierce loue congeales an Ice,
Which nor the force of fierce enflamed sunne
May thaw, nor may be moult with mightie flames,
Which frost doth make me quake like Aspen leaues.

Such time the windes are whist, and trembling leaues,
And beast grow mute reposing on the mountaines,
Then when aslaked beene the heauenly flames,
Both in the waine and prime tide of the yeare:
I watch, I warde, vntil the new sprung sunne,
And hope, and feare, and feele both cold and Ice.

But when againe her morrow-gathered Ice
The morne displaies, and frostieth drouping leaues,
And day renewes with rising of the sunne,
Then wailful forth I wend through vales and mountaines:
Ne other thought haue I day, moneth, and yeare,
But of my first the fatall inward flames.

Thus loue consumes me in his liuely flames,
Thus loue doth freeze me with his chillie Ice,
So that no time remaines me through the yeare
To make me blithe: ne are there any leaues:
Through al the trees that are vpon the mountaines,
That may conceale me from my sweetest sunne.

First shall the sunne be seene without his flame,
The wintred mountaines without frost or ice,
Leaues on the stones ere I content one yeare.

   This written in an amorous and more plausible vaine
(as that which most pleased the Ladies) and was not of
least worth, I haue set downe last.

O curious Gem how I enuie each while,
To see thee play vpon my Ladies paps,
And heare those Orbes where Cupid layes his traps
From whence a gratious Aprill still doth smile.

And now thou plaist thee in that Garden gentill,
Twixt golden fruite and neere her heart receiuest
Thy rest, and all her secret thoughts conceiuest
Vnder a vaile faire, white, diuine, and subtill.

Ye gentle pearles where ere did nature make you?
Or whether in Indian shoares you found your mould,
Or in those lands where spices serue for fuell:
Oh if I might from out your essence take you,
And turne my selfe to shape what ere I would,
How gladly would I be my Ladies Iewell?

   Many such like were deuised by *Minecius*, and allowed by *Philenia*, thorow which, Loue, that had newe

burgend his wings, began to flie, and being shut in
close embers, brake out to open fire: so that like the
Alcatras that scenteth farre, *Philenia* consented to yeeld
him fauour who sought it, knowing that his wit like the
rose being more sweet in the bud then in the floure
would best fit her: and as the hearb *Ephemerus* that
hath in his spring a sweete and purple floure, but beeing
of tenne dayes growth conceiueth nothing of beauty,
but is replenished with barrennesse, so course of time
woulde change him; she made choice of him, since in
that estate of life wherein he then liued, was fashioned
to all pleasures, and disfurnished of no perfection, she
knew him most meetest to enioy hir beautie, and most
accordant to possesse her marriage bed.

But leaue we *Philenia* delighted in her *Minecius*,
Margarita applauding them both, *Protomachus* conuersing with *Arsinous*, and the whole courtely traine of
Mosco liuing in their content; and let vs haue an eie to
Cusco and the emperour thereof, who no sooner arrived
in this court, but like the good gardner, knowing his
time to plant; like the fortunate husband well trained to
yoake and plough, learned of *Trifolium*, who lifteth vp
her leaues against tempest; and the emet, who by her
prouision and trauel foretelleth a showre and trouble
that followeth, thought good (hauing beene taught by
experience to take the opportunitie, knowing that princes and monarchs mindes are most subiect to alterations,
according to the humours of their counsailes) to send
his sonne *Arsadachus* to *Mosco*: whereupon furnishing
him with princely attendance and great treasures, he
set him forward on his way, and at his last farewel,
tooke his leaue of him in this fatherly and kingly manner: My sonne, as thou art yoong in yeres, so hast thou

K

yong thoughts, which if thou gouerne not with discretion, it will be the cause of thy destruction. Thou art
leauing thy country for an other court, thy familiars, for
new friends, where the least mite of follie in thee, will
shew a mountaine, the least blemish, a great blot. Since
therefore thine inclination is corrupt; and the faults
which I smother, in that I am thy father, others will
smite at, being thy foes: I will counsell thee to foresee
before thou fall; and to haue regarde before thy ruine.
Thou art borne a Prince, which being a benefit sent
from heauen, is likewise an estate, subiect to all vn-
happinesse; for, whereas much durt is, thither come
many carrions: where high fortunes, many flatterers;
where the huge cedar growes, the thistle springeth;
where the foorde is deepest, the fish are plentiest; and
whereas soueraigntie is, there are many seducers. Be
thou therefore warie like the Vnicorne, which, for feare
she should taste poison, toucheth with her horne, before
she lap it with her lippe, so seeme thou, in faining credit
to those, who meane to fawne on thee in thy error, to
discouer them in their flights, as the fowle *Anthias* doth
the Locust, and preuent them in their subtilties; as the
fish *Nibias* doth the sea dragon. In chusing thy friends,
learn of *Augustus* the Romane Emperour, who was
strange and scrupulous in accepting friends, but change-
lesse and resolute in keeping them. Chuse not such
companions, I pray thee, as will be drunke with thee
for good fellowshippe, and double with thee in thine
affaires; but use such as the thriftier sort doe by their
threede-bare coates, which being without wooll, they
cast off, as things vnfit for their wearing. And especially remember these short lessons, which the shortnesse
of time maketh me vtter by a word, where indeede they

require a whole dayes worke; beware of ouer-trust, lest you commit the sweetest of your life to the credite of an vncertaine tongue. Vse all such courtiers as visit you, in like manner as Goldsmiths do their mettall, who trie it by the touchstone if it be forthall, and melt it in the fire, before they vouchsafe it the fashion; so doe thou, and if they be counterfeit, they will soone leaue thee; if faithfull, they will the more loue thee. Trust not too much to the eare, for it beguileth many; nor to the tongue, for it bewitcheth more. Strive not with time in thy affaires, but take leasure; for a thing hastily enterprised, is more hastily repented. In your counsailes, beware of too much affection: and in your actions be not too prowd; for the one will proue your little regard of conscience; the other the corruption of your nature. And since thou art going into a forren court, and must follow the direction of a second father, whose fauour if thou keepe, thou maist hap to be most famous, looke to thy selfe; for as *Plato* saith; to be a king, and to raigne; to serue, and be in fauour; to fight, and overcome, are three impossible things, and are onely distributed by fortune, and disturbed by her frowardnesse in following. Therefore (*Protomachus*) seeke in all things to follow his humour; for opinion is the chiefe step to preferment: and to be thought well of by the Prince, is no small profit; and if so be thou wilt please him, doe him many seruices, and giue him few words. In thy speech be deliberate, without bashfulnesse: in thy behauiour courtly, without pride; in thy apparell princely without excesse; in thy reuenges bolde, but not too bloody; in thy loue be curteous, and not troublesome, and rather deserue a becke by bashfulnesse, then a checke by over-boldnesse; for many which for good nurture haue by

Ladies at first beene stroakt with the hand, haue for their impudencie afterwardes bin kickt out with the heele, or at leastwise thrust out by the head. Let it not be said of thee as it was of *Hanibal* among the Carthaginians, that thou neither giue that which thou promisest to thy friends, neither keepest any couenant with thine enemies; lest through the one thou be accompted without faith, through the other vnworthy life. Faine would I speake more (my sonne) but time suffereth me not: wherefore I pray thee by our gods, who gaue thee me, haue respect vnto my counsailes, lest thou grieue me; for better is a sonne lost in the cradle, then lewd and dissolute in the kingdome. This saide, the old Emperour *Artosogon* with piteous teares watered the cheekes of his corrupt sonne *Arsadachus*, and committing him to the conduct of his followers, and his presence to the hands of the chiefe peeres, he carefully (suspecting the worst) returned to his court.

Arsadachus being thus deliuered of his father, fedde himselfe with his owne naturall follies; and as the bird *Lenca* flying toward the south foretelleth stormes; euen so his lewd thoughts aimed at nothing, but wickednesse were the euident signes of his sinister behauiour: for being well shaped by nature, there was not any man more estranged from nurture; so that it was to be feared, that he should sooner want matter to execute his dishonest mind vpon, then a dishonest mind to execute any lewd matter: for among the traine appointed by his father to attend him, he took no delight but in those who were most lasciuious, who ministring the occasions, bred in him an earnest desire to do ill. His crueltie he shadowed with a kind of courtly seueritie; his lust vnder the title of loue; his treasons under the pretext of true meaning: so like the faire lillie he cloaked his ſtincking scent with his white leafe; and like the bird *Acanthus* liuing among thornes, hee tooke no other pleasure then to conuerse among vnthrifts. The graue counsellers appointed him by his father he set light by: and like a second *Cataline* rather honoured him that did inuent newe mischiefe, then countenance those who did perswade him from his corrupt manners. From this so sowre a ſtocke what fruit may be expected but crabbes? from so lewd beginnings, how lamentable issues? At laſt, arriuing in *Mosco*, he was informed of the emperours being in the caſtle of *Arsinous*: whervpon addressing himselfe thither according to the mightinesse of his eſtate, he was by *Protomachus* entertained royally, who receiuing the presents of *Artosogon*, returned them backe, who brought them with high rewards, chusing among al the princely gentlemen of his court, those for to accompany *Arsadachus* who were vertuously disposed and wel indewed. Among the reſt *Minecius* was appointed chiefe, whom *Margarita* highly truſted by reason of the trial *Philenia* had made of him. But among all other subtile demeanours in Court, this one was moſt to be admired, that *Arsadachus* shoulde make signes of great deuotion toward *Margarita*, and deluded her with moſt hatefull doublenesse; it was wonderfull to see him counterfet sighes, to faine loue, dissemble teares, to worke treasons, vow much, performe little; in briefe, vow al faith, and performe nothing but falshoode. *Margarita* (poore princesse) thinking all that golde which glittered; the ſtone pretious, by reason of his faire foile; the water shallowe, by reason of his milde silence, truſted so long, vntil she perished in her truſt, wholy ignorant that loue is like the sea-ſtarre, which whatso-

euer it toucheth it burneth: for knowing the resolution
of her father, the conclusion of the nobilitie, she beganne to ſtraine her thoughts to the higheſt reach,
fancying euery motion, wincke, becke, and action of the
Cuscan Prince, in such sort as that (assiſted by the
vertuous, conſtant, and vnspotted simplicitie of her
nature) she seemed not to suspect whateuer she saw, nor
to count it wrong, howsoeuer shee endured. Among all
other the counsellers of this yoong and vntoward heire
(about that time the flame of his follie long time smothered, beganne to smoake, besides his owne countrie-
men, which were *Brasidas*, *Capaneus*, and other) there
liued a great Prince in the court of *Protomachus*, who
delighted rather to flatter then counsell, to feede cor-
ruptions then purge them, who had *Macheuils* prince in
his bosome to giue inſtance, and mother *Nana* the
Italian bawd in his pocket to shew his artificall villanies.
This Thebion being in high account with the Emperour for his ripe wit, was quickely entertained by this
vngracious Prince for his cunning wickednesse; who
where *Arsadachus* was prone by nature to doe ill, neuer
ceased to miniſter him an occasion of doing ill. For,
perceiuing one day how with ouer-luſtful eies yᵉ yong
prince beheld *Philenia*, egged him onward which had
too sharp an edge, vsing old prouerbs to confirme his
odious discourses and purposes: to be briefe, *Arsadachus*
perceiuing *Philenia* and *Margarita* always conuersant,
resorted often to them, giuing the Emperours daughter
the hand for a fashion, whileſt *Arsinous* darling had the
heart for a fauour. And the better to cloke this corruption, he vsed *Minecius* with more then accuſtomed fa-
miliarity, seeming to be very importunate in his behalfe
with *Philenia*, where indeede he only sought opportun-

itie to discouer his owne loue. Whereuppon beeing one
day desired by *Minecius* to worke a reconcilement betweene him and his miſtresse, by reason he knew him
to be both eloquent and learned; hee taking the occasion at a certaine feſtiuall, whileſt *Minecius* courted *Margarita*, to withdraw *Philenia* to a bay window in the
caſtle, which ouerlooked the faire fieldes on euery side;
where taking her by the hand he beganne thus:

Beautifull *Philenia*, if I knew you as secret as you are
sage, I would discouer that to you in wordes, which I
couer in my heart with sighes. If it bee loue, great
prince, (saide *Philenia* little suspecting his treacherie)
you may commend it to my eare, in that it is setled in
this heart; as for silence, it is louers science, who are as
curious to conceale, as cunning to conceiue: and as
Hunters carrie the feather of an Egle againſt thunder,
so louers beare the hearbe *Therbis* in their mouthes,
which hath the vertue to ſtay the tongue from discourse
whileſt it detaineth the heart with incredible pleasure.
If it be so saide *Arsadachus*, blushing very vehemently
(for natures sparkes of hope were not as yet altogether
ruinated) I will holde Ladies weakenesse for worth, and
disclose that secret which I thought to keep close. And
what is that quoth *Philenia?* Loue saide *Arsadachus*, it is
loue, and there hee pawsed. Loue, my Lord (quoth the
Lady) why it is a passion full of pleasure, a god full of
goodnes; and truſt me, *Margarita* hath of late dayes
ſtollen him from his mother at *Paphos*, to make him her
play-fellow in *Mosco*, she proineth his winges euerie day,
and curleth his lockes euerie houre; if he crie, she ſtilles
him vnder your name, if he be wanton, she charmes
him, with thinking on you: since then she hath the
sicknesse in her hand, that loueth you in her heart;

complaine not of loue since you command it. Here *Arsadachus* vnable to endure the heate of affection, or conceale the humour that restrained him, brake off hir discourse in this sort: Ah *Philenia*, if I did not hope, that as the hard oake nourisheth the soft silke-worme; the sharpe beech bringeth forth the sauourie ches-nut, the blacke *Bdellium* sweete gumme; so beautiful lookes concealed pittifull hearts, I would surffet in my sorrowes to the death, rather then satisfie thee in my discourse. But hoping of thy silence (*Philenia*) I wil disclose my minde: I loue *Philenia*; faire *Philenia*, I loue thee; as for *Margarita*, though she cherish beauty in her bosome, thou inclosest him in thy beutie; she may haue his feathers, but thou his fancies; she may please him well, but thou onely appease him. You do speake Greeke *Arsadachus* (saide *Philenia*) I vnderstand you not, I will paraphrase on it then (quoth the Prince) to make it plainer (for now occasion had emboldned him.) I come not to pleade a reconcilement for *Minecius*, as you suppose, but remorse for my selfe (sweete madam) on set purpose, for vpon you (faire madam) dependeth my life, in your handes consisteth my libertie; your lookes may deifie my delights; your loures dare me with discontents. I pray thee therefore, deere *Philenia*, by those chaste eies (the earnest of my happines) by this faire haire (the minister of all fauours) take compassion of *Arsadachus*, who being a prince, may preferre thee, and an emperour, wil loue thee: as for *Margarita*, let *Minecius* and her accord them, for onely I will make thee empresse, and she may make *Minecius* Emperour. *Philenia* vnable to indure his diuelish and damned assaults, flang from him with this bitter and sharpe answere: Did not my promise locke vppe these lippes (thou iniurious Prince) thy doublenes shoulde be as well knowne in this Court as thy name; but since my promises haue made thee presumptuous, I will heereafter heare before I answere, and trie before I trust. Is this the faith thou bearest to *Margarita*? thy friendship thou vowest to *Minecius*, to falsifie thy faith to one, and delude the trust of the other? Hence, poisoned, because I abhorre thee; and if heereafter thou haunt me with these lewd and lecherous salutes, trust me, the Emperour shall know thy treasons, and others shall bee reuenged on thee for thy treacheries. This saide, she thrust into the company of other Ladies, leauing him altogether confused: yet being made confident, by reason of her promise, he withdrew himselfe to his chamber, where tossing his licentious limmes on his soft bed, he fed on his desperate determination, till *Thebion* and *Brasidas* (the one a Cuscan, and the other a Moscouian, both of his dissolute counsell) entred his chamber: who after they had sounded the cause of his sorrowes, and the manner of the disease, quickly ministred the methode of curing it: for the day of *Minecius* marriage being at hand, and the nuptiall feast ordained the Monday following: they seeing the grounded affection of the Prince, concluded this; by the death of *Minecius* to minister *Arsadachus* his remedie, the complot whereof they layde in this sort: that (where in Mosco it was accustomed, that such nobles as married yong heires in their fathers house, shoulde after the ioyning of hands conduct them to their owne castles, there to accomplish the festiualles;) *Arsadachus* and they his counsellers with the assistance of their followers should lie in wait in the woodes of Mesphos, by which *Minecius* and his bride should needly passe, where they might surprise *Philenia*, and murther *Minecius*.

Arsadachus too toward in all tyranny, no sooner conceiued the manner, then consented to the murther: and
hauing a subtile and preuenting wit (and being very
carefull howe to acquit himselfe of the matter) he asked
Thebion how he should answere *Protomachus*. Tut said
he, feare not that, for in the enterprise you shall be disguised, and *Brasidas* here your true counseller shall
onely take the matter on him, and flee into Cusco, where
your credit can countenance him against all iustice: for
your selfe, fashion your minde for these few dayes to
please *Margarita*, to appease *Philenia*, to further *Minecius*; seeme likewise discontented with your former
motions, so shall you rid suspect in them, and be more
readie in your selfe to effect; seeme now to be more
deuout to the gods then euer, for this opinion of deuotion is a great step to performe any waighty action: for
where we offer much to the gods who are most pure,
our actions are least suspected; and reuenge is better
performed in the Temple where wee pray, then in the
field where wee fight: for the offender in that place
trusteth sufficiently to his forces, wherein the defender
presumeth too much on his deuotion. Tut the king that
nipt *Acsculapius* by the beard, gaue instance to those
that follow to gripe the enemie by the heart. But
(mightie prince) I must ende with &c. *Arsadachus*
knowing the cloth by the list, the bill by the *Item*, the
steele by the marke, and the work by the words, with a
smile commended that which was concluded; and thereupon hasted to Court, where finding *Margarita*, *Philenia*, and *Minecius* in the priuie garden, he counterfeiting
maruellous melancholie, hauing his coate sutable to his
conceit, presented both the Ladies with this melancholie,
which *Minecius* ouerreading most highly commended.

My words, my thoughts, my vowes,
Haue soild, haue forst, haue stainde,
My tongue, my heart, my browes.

My tongue, my heart, my browes,
Shall speake, shall thinke, shall smile,
Gainst words, gainst thoughts, gainst vowes.

For words, for thoughts, for vowes,
Haue soiled, wrongde, and stained,
My tongue, my heart, my browes.

Whereon henceforth I sweare:
My words, my thoughts, my vowes,
So vaine, so vile, so bace,
Which brought, my tongue, heart, browes,
To shame, repulse, disgrace.

Shall euermore forbeare,
To tempt that brow, that heart, that tongue, so holy,
With vows, with thoughts, with words, of too great folly.

Margarita ouerreading this sonet, supposed it to be
some melancholie report of his prettie wanton discourses
with her, whereupon she spake thus: *Arsadachus* were
I the priest to confesse you, you should haue but small
pennance; since in loue (as *Philostratus* saith) *Cupid* dis-
penseth with an oth, and words are good weapons to
winne women, but if either of these haue defaulted in
you, blush not, they shall be borne withal, for as the
Mole hath foure feete and no eies; so a louer may be
borne withall, for one maistaking among a many ver-

tues: to be briefe as the Logicians say passion is no
more but the effect of action, the one whereof I haue
gathered in these lines, the other thou must shew in thy
life: this said she ceased, and *Philenia* blushed. *Minecius*
to cut off these mute melancholies of his mistresse gaue
the dagger a new haft, turning ouer the leafe to a second
discourse, ministring *Arsadachus* by that meanes occasion to court *Margarita*, and himselfe opportunitie to
pacifie *Philenia*, who by the carriage of her eie, shewed
the discontent of her mind.   In short words *Arsadachus*
so behaued himselfe with his Mistresse, that neither
Tiberius for his eie, neither *Octauius* for his affabilitie,
neither *Alexander* for his scarre, nor *Cicero* for his mole,
were so much commended, and noted, as the yong
Cuscan was for his behauior. Lord how demurely would
he loooke, when he thought most deuillishly? how could
he fashion himself to haunt there, where he did most
hate? to smooth choler vnder colour of friendship? so
that *Margarita*, laughed for ioy, to see his grauitie,
Minecius admired to behold his demeanour; but *Philenia* mistrusted his double and sinister subtilties. In a
word, as the day succeedeth the night, and the shutting
vp of the euening, is followed by the serenitie of the
morning, so time passed, so long, til the present day
aproched, wherein the marriage was to be solemnised:
whereon the emperor (the more to dignifie the nuptials)
countenanced the marriage with his presence. Thither
likewise resembled the flower of the nobilitie and
Ladies; among whom *Margarita* was not least sumptuous, for on that day hir apparel was so admirable, hir
cariage and behauior so execelent, that had the wisest
Cato beheld her, he would haue in some parte dismissed
his stoical seueritie: hir golden haires curled in rich

knots, and enterlaced with rich bands of diamonds and
rubies, seemed to ſtaine *Apollos* golden bush; enuirond
with hir wreath of chrisolites, her eies like pure carbuncles, seemed to smile on the roses of her cheekes,
which consorted with the beautie of the lillie, made her
beutie more excelent, her eies, briars like the net of
Vulcan, polished out of refined threeds of fine ebonie,
her alablaſter neck was encompassed with a coller of
orient perle, which seemed to smile on her teeth when
she opened her mouth, claiming of them some con-
sanguinitie; her bodie was apparrelled in a faire loose
garment of greene damaske, cut vpon cloth of tissue,
and in euerie cut, was inchased a moſt curious Iewell,
wherein al the escapes of Iupiter, the wanton delights of
Venus, and the amorous deceits of *Cupid* were cunningly
wrought. Thus attired, she attended the bride, being
hir selfe waited on by a troupe of beautifull damsels that
day. *Arsadachus*, though with little deuotion accompanied the Emperour, being that day clothed in red cloth
of golde, betokening reuenge. It were a vaine matter to
reckon vp the order of the bridegroome, the maieſtie of
his fauorers, the maner of the lords and ladies, the
sumptuousnes of the feaſts and triumphs, the harmonie
and musicke in the temples; sufficeth it, that by the consent of *Arcinous*, *Philenia* was betrothed to *Minecius*,
who seeing the day welnigh spent, and the time conuenient to depart to his caſtell, (after he had with
humble reuerence inuited the emperor, his daughter,
with the other Princes the next day to his feſtival,
which he had prepared in his owne house) made all
things in a readines, and departed, hauing receiued by
the emperor and *Arcinous*, many rich rewards. *Arsada-*
chus seeing the long desired houre of his delights at

hand, ſtole out of the courte in great secret to his
lodging, where arming himselfe according as *Thebion*
had giuen him inſtructions; and attended by *Brasidas*
and other Cuscans, his truſtie followers, he presently
poſted into a groue, thorow which the new married
couple should needly passe, where he priuily hid himselfe and his ambush. By that time the bright and glorious light of heauen, abasing himselfe by degrees, reposed his sweatie ſteedes in the soft bosome of cleere
looking *Eurotas;* and euening the fore-messenger of the
night had haled some ſtarres to illuminate the hemisphere, when as *Minecius* (in the top of al his felicities)
accompanied with his faire *Philenia* and other folowers,
without either suspect of treason or other trouble entred
the wood, and through the secretnesse thereof, hied
them toward their determined abode. But al the way
Philenia took no comfort, dreadfully suspecting the
subtile dealings of *Arsinous;* and oft she sighed, and
often she dropt downe lillies on the roses of her face, or
rather, such sweete teares wherewith the blushing morne
enchaseth the soft *Hyacinth. Minecius* seeing her in these
passions, perswaded her vnto patience: but euen as
(according to the opinion of *Aristotle*) lions, beares,
eagles, griffins, and al other birds and beaſts whatsoeuer, are then more egre and cruel when they haue yong
ones: so *Philenia* hauing now a second care annexed to
her owne safetie, (which was for her deere husband)
could not cease to perplexe her selfe, and to feare for
him. Long had they not trauelled, but they discouered
the ambush, and the ambush assaulted them: among
which *Arsadachus* greatly disguised, as he that enuied
the fortunes of *Minecius,* tooke holde on the reines of
Phileniaes palfrey, whileſt *Thebion,* and *Brasidas,* with

others, with their naked swordes beganne to assault *Minecius* and his followers. He that hath seene the faulcon seizing his keene talents in the flesh of a sillie doue, and playing his sharp bill on her soft feathers, might haue thought on *Arsadachus*, who no sooner tooke holde on her, but pulling the maske from her face, enforced many violent kisses on her soft lips, whilest she exclaiming on the name of *Minecius*, and crying, help, repulsed the iniuries with her white hands, which were iniuriously offred to her delicate face. *Minecius* suspecting no more then was true, and vnable to endure further violence, deemed it greater honor to die in defence of his mistresse, then beholde the impeach of her credit, left his companions who fled, and with naked sword smote *Arsadachus* a mightie blowe on the helme, through which he staggered, and lost his hold-fast; then renewing his mistresse which was almost dead for feare, hee boldly spake thus to *Arsadachus*; Traitor, and coward, that in time of peace goest thus armed, and with vniust armes assaultest naked knights, if any sparke of honor raigne in thee, giue me armes and weapons; if thou seek my life, take it from me with courage like a knight, not by treason like a coward; if my Loue, I pray thee take these eies from their sight, these handes from their sense, and this tongue from his speech: for whilest the one may see, the other fight, and the third threaten: thou shalt haue no part of that wherein my felicity is reposed; thus saying, he remounted *Philenia:* whilest he was thus occupied, *Arsadachus* swelling with impatience after he had bin animated by his followers, replied thus: Soft (amorous sir) this is no meate for your mowing, you best were rather to fall to your prayers, then to vse prating, to beseech for life,

then to seech loue: for assure thy selfe, there is no way
with thee but death, nor no loue for *Philenia* but mine.
This said, he gaue *Minecius* a mightie ſtroake on the
head, so that the blood ouerflowed his coſtly attire, and
he fell to the ground. *Philenia* halfe madde with melancholie, leapt from her palfrey to comfort her paramour;
and seeing the whole troope of assailants ready to charge
her husband, and assured that *Arsadachus* was the chiefe
of them, with such a piteous looke as *Venus* caſt on
bleeding *Adonis* shee behelde *Minecius*, and wiping his
wounds with one hand, and touching the knees of
Arsadachus with the other, she spake thus: Ah Cuscan
prince though thy face is shadowed, I knowe thee by
these follies, though thy raiments are changed, I iudge
thee by thy rashnesse, what seekeſt thou? if my fauour,
it is already bequeathed: if reuenge, how base is it
againſt a woman? if Minecius life, how iniurious art
thou to wrong him that loues thee as his life? Ah cruell
as thou art (yet would thou wert not cruel) thou knoweſt *Chrises* teares could moue *Achilles*, the one proceed-
ing from a seely maid, the other pitied by a princely
man: thou knoweſt that *Alexander* to *Campaspe*, *Pompey*
to his prisoner, and other great conquerours haue rather shewed compassion then victorie, and wilt thou
who art equall to all in power, be inferior to al in vertue?
Ah wo is me poore *Philenia* that haue planted my affections there where they are watered with warme blood,
and heape my compassion there where working teares
haue no boote. I pray thee gracious prince, I pray thee
be gracious: diuide not those by murther, whome the
gods haue vnited by marriage: seperat not those soules
by death whome the deſtinies haue appointed to liue. In
speaking these words she beheld *Minecius*, who through

the grieuousnesse of his wounds, fell in a swowne: whereupon she casting off all care of life, and hope of comfort, closed her soft lippes to his, breathing the balme of her sighes into his breathlesse bodie, clapping his pale cheekes with her pretie hands, moisting his closed eies, with her christal teares, so that they who were the very authors of her sorow, gan sigh to see her ceremonies. Wilt thou hence (said she) *Minecius?* Oh stay for *Philenia*, let our soules post together to *Elizium* that on earth here may not enioy their happinesse; for nothing shall separate me from thee (my loue:) if thou do banish sight from thine eie, I will driue out blood from my heart: if thy beautie grow pale as nying death, my cheekes shall pine as seeking death: if thou faint through feeblenesse of bodie, I will default through waightinesse of discontent: and since we may not liue together, we will die together. With this *Minecius* rowsed himselfe: and *Arsadachus* inflamed, replied; *Philenia*, there is no raunsome of thy husbands life, but thy loue, nor no meanes to pacifie me, but my pleasure of thee: speake therefore, and sound the sentence of my delight, or *Minecius* destruction: which said, he approched to kisse hir: whom *Minecius* though halfe dead beganne to rescue: and *Philenia* halfe bedlam enforced her selfe in these termes: Traitor disloyall and damned leacher, since neither teares, nor tearmes will satisfie thee, vse thy tyranny (for better were it for me to be buried with honor, then bedded with infamie) do therefore thy worst, thou hated of the gods, and despised among men, for no sooner shalt thou assaile my husband, but thou shalt slaie me: each drop of his blood shall be doubled by mine: and as in life he should haue beene the shelter of mine honor, so euen in death wil I

be the shield to defend him frõ the assaults of his enemies: come therefore ye murtherers, in growing cruel
to me, you wil proue pitiful: first take my life, that
Minecius beholding my constancie, may die with more
comfort. Thus cried she out with many teares; and *Minecius* disswaded her. But the time passing away, and
Arsadachus fearing delaies, seeing all hope lost, grew to
desperate furie, so that animating his followers, they
set on *Minecius*, who valiantly defended himselfe. It was
a world to see, how during the conflict *Philenia* bestirred her, letting no blow slip without the warde of
her body, lying betweene the sword of the enemy for
her husbands safetie, crying out on the heauens til she
was wellnie hoarse with crying. At last *Minecius* lacking
blood, *Philenia* breath, both of them entangled arme in
arme, fell downe dead, leauing the memorie of their
vertues to be eternized in all ages. *Arsadachus* seeing
the tragedies perfourmed (not without some sighs
which compassion extorted from him, as strokes do fire
out of hard flint) he presently sent *Brasidas* away, as it
was concluded (attended by those Cuscans that followed him in the enterprise) and hee with *Thebion* speedily
posted to their lodging, both vndiscouered and vnsuspected.

By this, such as attended *Minecius* to his castle had
with speedy flight entred the court of *Arsinous;* who
certified of his daughters danger, aduised the emperour,
and presently with certaine armed souldiers, posted on
to the rescouse: meane while *Protomachus* made search
through al the court for such as were absent; and they
that were appointed to the action entring *Arsadachus*
chamber, found him in his fore sleepe: where-through

the emperour being aduertised, gan little suspect him: in like sort found they *Thebion*, only *Brasidas* was missing. In the meanewhile *Arsinous* hauing attained the place of the conflict, found both the murthered bodies sweltered in their blouds: whereupon falling from his horse in great furie, he thus exclaimed on fortune. Oh fortune, wel art thou called, the enemie of vertue, since thou neither fauourest such as deserue wel, nor destroyest those that performe ill; for hadst thou not beene parciall, my daughters chastitie had preuented her death, and her murtherers crueltie had beene their owne confusion: woe is me that haue lost my floure in the bud, my hope in the eare, and my haruest in the blossome. Ah my deere *Philenia*, deare wert thou to me, that bought thee with much care, and haue lost thee with more: deere wert thou vnto me, who hast cost me many broken sleepes to bring thee vp, many carefull thoughts to bestow thee, more fatherly teares to preuent thy ouerthrow, and now hauing reared the fortresse of my delights, the tempest of iniurious fortune hath destroyed it: wo is me that am carefull to publish my paines, and negligent to seeke remedy; fond am I to defie fortune from whom I cannot flie: ah *Arsinous* weep not her that may not be recalled with teares, but seeke to reuenge her; shew thy selfe rather fatherly in act, then effeminate in teares? Which said, he gouerned himselfe, causing the dead bodies honorably to be couered and conueied with him to his castle, where within a temple erected to chastitie, hee reared a faire tombe of white marble, wherein with the generall teares of the emperour and his whole court, these two faithful louers were entombed, and ouer their graues thus written:

Vertue is dead, and here she is enshrined,
  Within two lifelesse bodies late deceased:
Beautie is dead, and here is faith assigned
  To weepe her wracke, who when these died first ceased,
    Pitie was dead when tyranny first slew them,
    And heauen inioies their soules, tho earth doth rew
                                                    (them,
Since beautie then and vertue are departed,
  And faith growes faint to weep in these their fading,
And vertuous pitie kind and tender hearted,
  Died to behold fierce furies fell inuading.

    Vouchsafe ye heuens that fame may haue in keeping
    Their happy and thrice blessed names, for whome
    Both vertue, beautie, pittie died with weeping,
    And faith is closed in this marble tombe.

This register of his loue did *Arsinous* with many
teares write vpon the toombe of his deceased sonne in
law and daughter, who had no sooner furnished the
funeralles, but *Phidias* a page of *Philenias*, who during
the mortall debate, and bloudy massacre, had hid himself in a thicket, and ouerheard the whole discourse of
Arsadachus, repaired to the court, who calling *Arsinous*
aside, with pitious teares discoursed vnto him the whole
tragedy in such ruthfull manner, as that it was hard to
say, whether the lad in bewraying it, or the father in
hearing it, were more compassionate. The old man certified the truth, though scarce able, yet smothered his
griefes, till oportunitie offered, suffering the emperour
(like a wise man) to follow his owne course, who the
next morning assembling his nobilitie, forgot not *Arsadachus*, who making semblance to haue but new inteli-

gence of the murther of *Minecius* and his loue, repaired
to the Court in mourning apparrell, and being present
when the matter was debated, seemed to weepe bitterlie,
crying out on the emperour for Iuſtice, exclaiming on
the iniquitie of time, the crueltie of men, and tyrany of
loue. *Protomachus* was not a little pleased herewith, neither was *Margarita*, aggreeued to heare it, but *Arsinous*
boyled in choler to see it: at laſt it was found out by a
scarfe which *Brasidas* had let fall (and was after taken
vp by one of those who fled) that he was at the murther,
whereupon his absence was sufficient to conuict him,
and *Arsadachus* called forth to answere for him in that
he was his attendant, spake thus: Noble emperor, the
gods that haue placed thee in thy kingdome, shall beare
me witnes, how I grieue this accident, and willingly
would reuenge it, and since my follower to my defame,
hath (as it is supposed) bin a principall, vouchsafe me
noble emperour licence for a time to depart to *Cusco*,
where I will both discharge my choller, purge my
griefe, and be so reuenged of *Brasidas* (who as I heare
is fled, and by the token is guilty) as all the world shall
ring of the iuſtice, and ridde me of suspicion. The emperour not hearing one that dared say his letters should
suffice, endeuouring himselfe to seeke the confederates;
and because by his lookes he perceiued some discontents in *Arsadachus*, he sought al the means he could to
please him, and remembring himselfe (that those good
deeds which are done to our self beloued, are eſteemed
as to our selfe) he highly promoted *Thebion*, thinking
thereby to winne the heart of *Arsadachus*, so that he
pretermitted no consultations, where *Thebion* was not
chiefe, neither beſtowed benefits, wherein he had no
part. The yong prince measuring al this according to

the coruption of his nature, supposed these fauors were but to sound him, and that *Thebion* being wonne by benefits, would easily consent to bewray him, whereupon he conceiued a deadly hate against him, and perseuered it so long till he effected it in this manner to his death: For knowing that *Margarita* deerely loued him, ayming all her fashions to his fancies, hir behauiours, to his humors, he began anew to cloake with her, shewing her so vndoubted signes of assured affection, that she seemed in a paradise of pleasure, to see his pliantnes, and hauing with sweete words, trained her to his lewer, he attended such an occasion, as that he found her alone walking in the priuie garden in her meditations, (for those that loue much, meditate oft) where nying her with a courtly salute, he thus found her affection: Faire Princesse, if either my vnfained loue haue any force, or your vertuous nature true compassion, I hope both my sorrowes shal be pittied, and my discontents succored. Why what aggreeueth my deere Lord said *Margarita*? (and heartily she sighed in saying so) is either our court vnpleasant, our entertainement vnworthie, our ladies vnapt to worke your delights? beleeue me good prince, if Mosco cannot suffice to please you, *Europe* and the worlde shall be sought to satisfie you. Kinde words good madam, said *Arsadachus*, act and silence must content me, which if you will vnder the faith of a noble and famous princesse promise me, I shall be beades man, to pray for your happinesse, and rest yours vnfained in all seruice and loyaltie. *Margarita* hauing gotten such an oportunitie to please him both vowed and reuowed all secrecie, swearing although it were with the hasard of hir life to do whatsoeuer him best liked, and conceale what so it please him to discouer, so great is the simplicitie of women, who are soone led where they most like. *Arsadachus* finding the iron hot, thought good to strike; the fruit ripe, began to gather, the floure springing, ceased not to water: and thus began to worke her. True it is madam, that where loue hath supremacie, all other affections attend on it, so that neither the eie beholdeth, neither the sent smelleth, nor the eare heareth, neither the tongue speaketh any thing, but is to the honour of the best beloued: this finde I true in my selfe, who since I surrendred you the fort of my fancie, finde my delights metamorphosed into yours, yet so much am I tied vnto you, as that danger which either attempteth or toucheth you, or any of yours, wholly attainteth me. The proofe wherof you may perceiue in this, that hauing heard through my intire acquaintance with *Thebion*, a certaine resolued determination in him, to make your father away, by reason of his familiar accesse to his maiestie euerie morning, I could not choose but discouer his drift vnto you sweete Princesse, whose dangers must needely second your fathers subuersion. *Thebion* said *Margarita*, alas my lord what reason should moue him hereunto, since no one is more fauoured by my father then he? can fauour possibly be requited with such falshood? Doubt you it said *Arsadachus*? why madam where is greater treason, then there where is least mistrust? vnder the cleare Christall lurketh the mortall worme, vnder the greene leafe the greedie serpent, and in fairest bosomes are falcest hearts. Thinke not that liberallitie hath any power in depraued minds, for whereas the thoughts hant after emperie, hemd are each supposes, faith dieth, truth is exiled *nulla fides regni*, if you haue read histories, you shall finde that they soonest haue supplanted their Princes, who haue bin least sus-

pected, as may appeare by *Giges*, and other: cast therefore hence (my deare ladie) all thought of excuse, and
bethinke you of preuention; for it is greater wisedome,
to see and preuent, then to heare and neglect. *Thebion*
hath conspired and doth conspire, resoluing with himselfe to vsurp the empire, murther *Protomachus*, banish
you; all which I haue learned of him, dissembling my
affections towards you, and soothing him in his corrup-
tions; yea so farre haue I brought him, and so neere
haue I wrought it, that I can assure you to morrow
morning is the last of your fathers life, vnlesse you preuent it. Alas my lord (said *Margarita* weeping) how
may this be? Thus my sweete loue and thus it is concluded (quoth *Arsadachus*) you know he hath euerie
morning of late priuate accesse vnto your fathers chamber, where being alone with him and the vnsuspected
emperour in his bed, he hath resolued with his dagger
to stabbe him to the heart; which secret, since the gods
haue opened vnto me, I think good to discouer vnto
thee (my deere heart) the meanes to preuent (which
shall the more easily be performed if thus you worke it)
no sooner let the day appeare, but in the morning betimes enter you your fathers chamber, where after you
haue saluted him, you may seeme to vtter this; that in a
dreame this night you were mightily troubled about his
Maiestie, and so troubled, that you thought *Thebion*
entring his chamber with a hidden poiniard stabbed
him to the heart. But what needes these circumlocutions
or delaies quoth *Margarita* if the treason be so manifest?
My lord, if it please you I will discouer it presently and
plainely. The gods forbid (said *Arsadachus*) that my
desires should be so hindered, for (my noble princesse)
the delay I seeke, and the order I prescribe you, is ra-

ther to ground your fathers affection towards me, and get the credite of this seruice then otherwise; yea the loue I beare thee sweete Ladie; (with that hee sighed and sealed it with a kisse) for hauing by this meanes wonne fauour, both our fortunes shall be bettered, our marriage hasted, and our fames magnified.

Margarita (poore princesse) supposing all that golde that glistered, yeelded easie consent; whereupon after many amorous promises, the yong prince tooke his leaue, willing her to be carefull in the morning, and to leaue the rest of the affaires to his faithfulnesse, and thus they parted.

But marke the nature of malice (which as the poet describeth is sleepelesse, restlesse and insatiate) for *Arsadachus* being departed from *Margarita*, and earnestly bent on his reuenge, sought out *Thasilides* the page of *Thebion*, whom he so cunningly wrought with othes, gifts, and gold, that he made him both promise and practise the meanes to put a certaine scedule into the pocket of his masters gowne which he vsually ware, the which he himselfe had wrote, and wherein he behaued himselfe with such art, as that he had not only counterfeted *Thebions* hand, but also the names of al such as either he thought his fauorites, or else likely to thwart his proceedings in court, among which hee forgote not *Ctesides* a graue counseller of the emperors, who the day before was very earnest with *Protomacus* to marry his daughter, shewing him euident reasons of *Arsadachus* counterfeiting. All these things falling out according to his own deuise and fantasie, he sought out *Thebion* that night, whom he vsed with the greatest familiaritie that might be: and to insinuate the more into his fauour, hee bestowed on him a poiniard, whose pummel was a bright carbuncle, the haft vnicorns horne, a iewell which *Thebion* had long time greatly desired, praying him of all loues to weare it for his sake; and since he was in such eſtimation to continue him in the good grace of the Emperour. *Thebion* made proud to be intreated and presented by so high a prince, promised both to weare his gift, and to winne him fauour. Wherevpon since the night was farre spent *Arsadachus* repaired to his lodging, *Thebion* to his reſt. But vaine is the hope that dependeth on the next day, and those worldly honours that doe wait on this life; for the one is preuented oftentimes by iniurious fortune, the other altered by our ouerweening miſtruſting words, actions, and desires, and shall manifeſtly appeare in the sequell of this historie. For no sooner gan bright day to chase away blacke darkenesse, and the ſtooping ſtares doe homage to the rising sunne, but *Margarita* arose, apparelling herselfe freshly like Maie, in a gowne of greene sendall, embrodered with all kind of floures in their natiue colours, and remembring her selfe of the affaire she had in hand; she vnder the conduct of loue (who is both a cunning dissembler and nice flatterer) haſted to her fathers chamber, and humbly admitted to the presence of the emperour by the groomes that attended him, (with a trembling hand, and a bashfull countenaunce: spreading the mute oratorie of her teares, vppon her blushing cheekes) she awoke him. *Protomachus* amased to see his daughters sodaine accesse, and sad countenance, began thus: How now my deere *Margarita*, what, hath loue awaked you this morning, threatning you with some apparant sorrow to make your after-good in deede more sauourie? why hangeth your countenance? why tremble your limmes? what moueth this your amasednes?

sweete maiden tell thy father. Ah my Lord (said *Margarita*) it is loue indeede that disturbes mee, but not that loue that is painted with feathers, wanton looks, that loue that whispereth affections in ladies eares, and whetteth womens wittes, making the eie traitor to the heart, and the heart betrothed to the eie; but that loue which was ingendred by nature, ordained by the heauens, attired by reuerence and duetie, and tired with nothing but death, that loue (and so speaking she wept) hath awaked me, to forewarne you. *Protomachus* somewhat vrged by these teares, rowzed himselfe on his pillow, and began more intentiuely to listen, asking her what had hapned? Ah deare father, said she, this night that is past I was greatly troubled with a grieuous dreame; me thought I saw *Thebion*, a man in high authoritie in your court, attended by many insolent rebels, who violently brake open your maiesties priuie chamber, murthered you in your bed, and dispossest me of my heritage, me thought euen then you cried vnto me; ah *Margarita* help me! and I with outcries calling for rescoue, *Arsadachus* came in hastily, who with his sword bereft *Thebion* of life, and me of feare: And so you waked and found all false (quoth the emperour) Tut, doate not on dreames, they are but fancies: and since I see (sweete daughter) that you are so troubled by night, I will shortly find out a yong prince to watch you, who shall driue away these night-sprights by his prowesse. Thus spake *Protomachus* smiling, yet smothered he suspect in his heart: for such as haue much, suspect much.

No sooner were these discourses finished, but *Arsadachus* knowing how to take his time, hastily approched the Emperors chamber, where intimating some occas-

ion of high import, he required to speake with *Protomachus*, and was presently let in. The Emperour conceiuing new suspicions vpon this second assault, beganne to misdeeme: and seeing *Arsadachus* with gastly
lookes entring the chamber, was ready to speake vnto
him when as the yong Cuscan preuented him, saying:
The gods be blessed (noble Emperor) that haue by
their foresight rid me of feare, and reft you of danger;
for sore haue I feared lest your maiestie should haue
perished before you had beene aduertised: Alas, why
in such dangers are you vnattended vpon, when the foe
is at the doore? why is not the guard in a readinesse?
Ah royall Moscouite rowze thee and arise, and honour
the sequele of the greatest treason that euer was contriued. Why what tidings bringeth *Arsadachus* said
Protomachus? Thus mighty prince (said he) yesternight
very late when I entred *Thebions* chamber vnawares, I
found his page (his master being absent) laying certaine
waste papers out of his pocket vpon his table, perusing
which, (as I was accustomed) by reason of the new
familiaritie betweene vs, I found one among the rest
where (alas that subiects should be so seditious) there
was a conspiracy signed by *Thebion*, *Ctesides*, and others
(whose names I remember not) to make your mightinesse away, and *Thebion* to enioy the crowne: the maner
to execute their stratageme, was when you least suspected, this morning; at which time *Thebion* by reason
of his neere familiaritie and accesse to you, should enter
your chamber and murther you. This paper when I had
ouer-read, I laide aside, making semblance of no suspition, resoluing this morning early to signifie the
whole vnto your maiestie, whose life is my libertie,
whose happines is my honour, whose death were my

vtter ruine and detriment. *Thebion* a traitor quoth *Protomachus;* are my fauours then so smally regarded? is my
curtesie rewarded with such cursednesse? Well *Arsadachus* (said he) happy art thou in bewraying it, and vnfortunate he and his confederates in attempting it, for
they all shall die.

This saide, he presently attired himselfe, laying certaine of his trustiest gentlemen in guard behinde the
tapistrie of his priuy closet, expecting the houre of a
most cruell reuenge: when as sodainely *Thebion* knock-
ed at the doore, and was presently admitted, who had
scarcely said, God saue the emperour, but euen in the
bending of his knees, hee was thrust through by *Arsadachus,* and the other of the guard hearing the broile,
came and mangled him in peeces, casting the residue to
the Emperours lions according as hee had appointed.
Protomachus grudging at the sodaine death of *Thebion,*
began to chide *Arsadachus* for his haste, saying, that it
was inconuenient for a subiect to be punished before
hee were conuicted. Conuicted (said *Arsadachus*) why
doth your grace suspect his guiltinesse? Beholde saide
hee (drawing out the poinyard which *Thebion* had at his
back) the instrumẽt that should haue slaine you, see
(saide hee) taking the schedule out of his pocket the
confederacie to betray you; and should such a wretch
liue then to iustifie? No (mightie Emperour) my soule
abhorres it; the care I haue of you will not suffer it; the
loue I beare *Margarita* will not indure it. The Emperour
ouer-reading the writing, and seeing the poinyard, gaue
credible beleefe, and with teares of ioy imbracing *Arsadachus* he said thus: Ah my sonne, the gods haue
blessed vs in sending vs such a friend, who hath saued
mee from imminent danger, and will make me fortun-

ate by marriage, hold take thee (said he) my *Margarita*, and with her, enioy my empire; and more, take thou my loue, which is so rooted in me toward thee, that death may not vntwine it. *Arsadachus* thanked the Emperour for this fauour, and recomforted *Margarita* with sweete words, being almost dead to see the stratageme passed. Meane while the Emperour gaue present direction to hang all the other conspirators, and put them to other tortures, who presently without knowing why, or licence to answere, were tyrannously executed; so great is the tyranny of princes which are subiect to light beliefe, and led by subtil suggestions.

The rumour of this accident spread through the Court, moued sundry imaginations in mens minds, some praised *Arsadachus*, some suspected the practise, all feared; for whereas iustice sleepeth being ouerborne with tyranny, the most secure haue cause to feare; among the rest *Arsinous* wept bitterly, knowing in himselfe the vertue of *Ctesides*, and remembring him of the murther of his deere *Philenia*, hee could not cease but welnie bedlam to crie out on the heauens, whose tragedie we must now prosecute, and leaue *Arsadachus* and his *Margarita* to their mery conceits and discourses.

Protomachus after that this late treason had beene discouered, beganne to be more warie, to keepe greater guard, and to vse *Arsinous* and the rest of the nobilitie with lesse familiaritie, who good old man, hauing before time beene shrewdly hurt, tooke this vnkindenesse to the heart (for where greatest loue is, there vnkindenesse is most grieuous) for that cause almost desperate he sought out the emperour, and finding opportunitie, he humbling him on his knees beganne thus: As *Traiane* (dread Monarch) was commended in Rome for hearing poore mens complaints, so art thou condemned in Mosco for shutting thy gates againſt all kind of sutors, so as (nowadayes) thou heareſt by others eares, workeſt by others hands, and speakeſt by others mouthes, where-through iuſtice is made a nose of waxe warmed, and wrought according to all mens pleasures, and the poore are left to complaine: the which the gods (if thou re-pent not) wil shortly punish in thee. Beleeue me (good Emperour) such as shut their gates againſt their sub-iects, cause them not to open their hearts willingly to obey them; and they that norish feare in their bosoms without cause, make themselues guilty of some crime by their suspect. Wherefore flieſt thou the sight of those that loue thee? shutting thy eares leſt thou heare those complaints that haue already deaffed the heauens for equitie. O prince, looke abroad, it behooueth thee; doe iuſtice, for it becommeth thee, and heare olde *Ar-sinous* a haplesse father; father doe I say, being thus robbed of my children? nay a desolate caitife, and doe me right. That iuſtice becommeth thee, marke these reasons: *Homer* desirous to exalt it, could not say more, but to call kings the children of the God *Iupiter*, and not for the naturalitie they haue, but for the office of iuſtice which they miniſter. *Plato* saieth, that the chiefeſt gift that the gods haue beſtowed on man is iuſtice; that therefore thou may seeme rightly descended of the gods, vouchsafe me audience, and to the end thou may boaſt thy selfe to enioy the leaſt gift of the gods, suc-cour me. Thou knoweſt my *Philenia* is slaine, but by whose hands thou knoweſt not; thou heareſt *Minecius* is murthered, but by whom thou enquireſt not, thou haſt rubbed the gall, but not recured the wounde; thou haſt tempered the medicine, but haſt not miniſtred it: yea thou haſt refreshed the memorie of my griefes very often, but remedied them neuer. Three moneths are paſt, since thou haſt made inquirie of my daughters death, and she that I nourished vp twentie yeares and better, is forgotten of all, but her olde father, lamented of none, but *Arsinous*: and can be reuenged by none but *Protomachus*. O Emperour I heare their discontented griefe crying out in mine eares, and appealing to thee by my tongue for iuſtice, me thinkes bloudlesse *Minecius* ſtandeth by thy throne vpbraiding thee of his seruices, and conuicting thee of ingratitude. *Philenia* crieth iuſtice *Protomachus*, iuſtice, not againſt *Brasidas*, who was but agent, but againſt *Arsadachus* the principall, that wretched *Arsadachus*, who in her life time assaied to moue her to luſt, and wrought her death, in that she would not consent to his luſt, againſt *Arsadachus* the viper nourished in your bosome, to poison your owne progenie, the locuſt dallied in *Margaritaes* lap, to depriue her of life. Ah, banish such a bewitched race of the Cuscans, I meane not out of your kingdome, but out of life; for he deserueth not to beholde the heauens, that conspireth againſt the gods, root out that bloodthirſty yongman, root out that murtherer, roote out that monſter, from the face of nature, that the poore deceased ghoſtes may be appeased, and their poore father pacified. Shew thy selfe a prince now *Protomachus*; the surgeon is knowen, not in curing a greene wound, but in healing a grieuous fiſtula; the warriour is knowne, not by conquering alittle village, but a great monarchie; and a prince is perceiued in preuenting a capitall peſtilence, not a priuate preiudice. That I accuse not *Arsadachus* wrongfully, behold my witnesses:

which saide, he brought out *Phileniaes* page, who con-
fidently and constantly auowed all he had told his master
in the presence of the emperour: wherefore (noble
monarch) haue compassion of me, and by punishing
this tragicke tyranny make way to thine owne eternitie.

Protomachus hearing this accusation was sorely
moued, now thinking all trueth which *Arsinous* had said
by reason of that vertue he had approued in him in
times past, now deeming it false, in that *Arsadachus* (as
he supposed) had lately and so luckily preserued him
from death. For which cause, calling the yong prince
vnto him, he vrged him with the murther before the
old man, and the yoong ladde his accuser, who shooke
off al their obiections with such constancie, that it was
to be wondered: what saith he *Protomachus*, am I, who
haue lately manifested my zeale in sauing your life
made subiect to the detraction of an old doting imagination with his pratling minister, I hope your Maiestie
(saith he) measureth not my credit so barely, neither
wil ouerslip this iniurie slightly, since you know, that
when the murder was done I was in my bed, when the
tragedie was published, I was the first that prosecuted
the reuenge; and more, the friendship twixt *Minecius*
and me should acquit me of this suspition. But it may
be, that this is some set match of *Thebions* confederates
that seeke my death, which if it shall be heere counten-
aunced, I will returne to Cusco, where I dare assure
my selfe against al such subtilties. This said, *Arsadachus* angerly departed: for which cause, *Protomachus*
fearing his speedy flight, sent *Margarita* to pacifie him;
and causing the tongue of the guiltlesse lad to be cut
out, and his eies to be prickt out with needles, both
which were guiltie (as he said) the one of pretended

M

seeing, the other of lewd vttering. He banished the olde Duke of Volgradia, who for all his faithfull seruices, had this lamentable recompence, and remoued himself, his court, and daughter to Mosco, where wee will leaue him a while.

Arsinous thus banished from the Court, after he had furnished himselfe of necessaries conuenient for his iourney, trauelled many a weary walke towards the desarts of Ruscia, crying out and exclaiming on the heauens for iustice; his hoarie lockes and bushy beard he carelesly suffered to grow (like to those Moscoes who are in disgrace with their emperors) seeming rather a sauage man than a ciuile magistrate (as in time past he had beene.) Long had hee not trauelled among many barren rockes and desolate mountaines, but at last hee arriued in a sollitarie Groue encompassed with huge hilles, from the toppes whereof, through the continuall frosts that fell, a huge riuer descended, which circling about a rocke of white marble, made it (as it were) an Island, but that to the northward there was a pretie passage of twelue foote broade, deckt with ranks of trees, which gaue a solitary accesse to the melancholie mansion; mansion I call it, for in the huge rocke was there cut out a square and curious chamber, with fine loopes to yeeld light, hewen thereout (as might be supposed) by some discontented wood-god wedded to wretchednesse. Here *Arsinous* seated himselfe, resoluing to spend the residue of his dayes in studies, praying to the gods continually for reuenge, and to the end (if happily any shoulde passe that way) that his deepe sorrow might be discouered, he with a punchion of steele in a table of white Alablaster engraued this ouer the entrance of his caue.

Domus doloris.

Who seekes the caue where horride care doth dwell,
  That feedes on sighes, and drinkes of bitter teares:
Who seekes in life to finde a liuing hell,
  Where he that liues, all liuing joy forbeares:
Who seeks that griefe, that griefe it selfe scarce knowes it,
  Here let him rest, this caue shall soone disclose it.

As is the mite vnto the sandie seas,
  As is the drop vnto the Ocean streames,
As to the orbe of heauen a sillie pease,
  As is the lampe to burning Ticius beames:
Euen such is thought that vainely doth indeuer,
  To thinke the care liues here, or count it euer.

Here sorrow, plague, dispaire, and fierce suspect,
  Here rage, here ielousie, here cursed spight,
Here murther, famine, treason and neglect,
  Haue left their stings to plague a wofull wight:
    That liues within this tombe of discontent,
    Yet loathes that life that nature hath him lent.

In this solitarie and vncouth receptacle, *Arsinous* liued, turning of his steede, to shift for foode amid the forest, and assending euerie day to the height of the rocke, hee shed manie salte teares before the Image of *Minecius* and *Philenia*, whose pictures he had brought with him from his castell, and erected there: and after his deuotions to the gods for reuenge, and to the ghosts to manifest his grief, he accustomed himself to walke in that desolate coppesse of wood, where sighing, he recounted the vnkindnes of his prince, the wretched-nes of his thoughts and life, melting away in such

melancholie, as the trees were amased to beholde it, and
the rockes wept their springs to heare it, as the Poe
saith, on a desolate and leauelesse oake he wrote this:

Thine age and wastfull tempests thee,
Mine age and wretched sorrowes me
                              defaced,
Thy sap by course of time is blent,
My sence by care and age is spent
                              and chased,
Thy leaues are fallen away to dust,
My yeares are thralld by time vniust.
Thy boughes the windes haue borne away,
My babes fierce murther did decay.
Thy rootes are firmed in the ground,
My rootes are rent, my comforts drownd,
                              showers cherish.
Thy barren bosome in the field,
                    I perish.
Since nothing may me comfort yeelde.

Storms, showers, age, weare, waste, daunt, and make the
     dry
Teares, cares, age, ice, waste, wring, and yet liue I.

In these melancholies leaue we the desolate duke c
Volgradia, till occasion be ministred to remember hin
and return we to *Margarita* and her louer. *Arsadacht*
reliant nowe in *Mosco*, whom *Protomachus* by reason c
the forepassed tragedies, thought to refresh with som
pleasant triumphs: for which cause he proclaimed
iusts throughout all the empire, assembling al th
Dukes, Lords, and gouernours of his prouinces, t

dignifie the open court he meant to keepe. Thither also
repaired all the faire ladies of *Moscouia*; among the rest
Margarita as one of most reckoning, made not the least
expence, for whatsoeuer, either to dignifie hir person,
or to set out her beautie, or to present her beloued,
could either be bought from *India*, traffiked in *Europe*,
or marchanded in *Asia*, was sought out, and especially
against the day of the tilt, and turny, at which time,
like a second *Diana*, hauing her goldilocks tied vp with
loose chaines of gold, and Diamondes, her bodie ap-
parreled in cloth of siluer, (ouer which she had cast a
vaile of blacke and golden tinsell, through which her
beautie appeared as doth the bright *Phœbus* in a summers morning: leauing our Hemisphere our faire
Hecate, chasing away balefull darkenesse with her bright
beames) shee was mounted on a high arch of triumph
couered with cloth of golde: neare vnto her sate her
olde father in his soueraigne maiestie; about her a
hundreth damselles in white cloth of tissue, ouer-cast
with a vaile of purple and greene silke loosly wouen,
carrying gold and siluer censors in their hands, from
whence issued most pleasant odours, such as in the
pride of the yeare breath along the coast of *Arabia Fœlix*
or drops from the balmie trees of the East.

Thus seated, the Challengers with their seuerall de-
uises entred the tilt-yard, each striuing so exceede other
in expence and excellence; whose trumpets cleered the
aire with their melodie. After these the Defendants
entred; among whom *Arsadachus* was chiefe, whose
pomp in that, exceeded al others I haue seene, and the
other are ordinarily matched in our Courts of christen-
dome, I will set downe vnto you. First, before the
triumph entred the tilt-yard, there was a whole volie of

a hundred cannons shot off; the noise whereof somewhat appeased, a hundred knights hauing their horse,
armes, crests, fethers, and each part of them couered
with greene cloth of golde, with lances of siluer, trotted
about the yard, making their steedes keepe footing,
according to the melodious sound of an orbe, which by
cunning of man, and wonderfull art was brought into
the presence of the prince. which whilst it continually
turned, presented all the shapes of the twelue signes
dauncing as it were to the harmonie, which the inclosed
musicke presented them. After these marched a hundred pages apparelled in white cloth of siluer with
crownets of siluer on their heads, leading each of them
in their right hands, a braue courser trapped in a capari-
son purple and gold; in their left, a scutchion with the
image of the princesse in the same. After these *Arsadachus* in his triumphant chariot drawen by foure white
vnicornes entred the tilt-yard, vnder his seate the image
of fortune, which he seemed to spurne, with this posie,
Quid hæc? on his right hand enuy, whom he frowned on
by hir this posie, *Nec hæc*; on his left hand the portrai-
ture of *Cupid*, by whome was written this posie, *Si hic*;
ouer his head the picture of *Margarita* with this mot,
Sola hæc. These armes were of beaten golde far more
curious then those that *Thetis* gaue hir *Achilles* before
Troy, or *Meriones* bestowed on *Vlysses* when he assaulted
Rhesus, being full of flames and half moones of saphires,
chrisolites, and diamonds. In his helme he bare his
mistresse fauour, which was a sleeue of salamanders
skinne richly perfumed, and set with rubies. In this sort
he presented him before the Emperour and his daughter, who was not alittle tickled with delight to behold
the excellencie of his triumph. The trumpets were

sounded, and the Iudges seated, *Arsadachus* mounted himselfe on a second *Bucephalus*, and taking a strong lance ouerbore *Stilconos* the earle of *Garauia*, breaking his arme in the fall; in the second encounter he ouer-threw *Asaphus* of *Tamiræ* horse and man, neither ceased hee till 20. of the brauest men at armes were vnhorsed by his hardinesse. All this while with blushes and sweete smiles *Margarita* fauored euery incountery, seeming with the egernesse of eie to breake euery push of the lance that leuelled at *Arsadachus*. His races being at end, *Plicotus* of *Macarah* entred the lists, who behaued himselfe like a braue prince, conquering as much with the sword, as the other with the lance: in this sort, this day, the next, and that which followed were ouerpast, wherein *Arsadach*. made euident proofes of great hope: so that *Protomachus* at the last cried out to his other princes; See ye Moscouites the hope of the empire, whose endings if they prooue answerable to his begin-nings, Europe may perhappes wonder, but never equall.

The third day being ended, and the honours be-stowed on them that best deserued them: the emperour in the chiefest of the festiuall caused the tables to be remoued, and the musicke to be called for; thinking by this meanes to giue loue more fuell, in hope it should burne more brighter: whereuppon the princes betooke them to daunce; and *Arsadachus* as chiefe, led *Margarita* the measures. And after the first pawse began thus with her; Princesse said he, by what means might loue be discouered if speech were not? By the eies (my lord said she) which are the keys of desire, which both open the way for loue to enter, and locke him vp when he is let in. Howe hap then (said he) that *Cupid* among the poets is fained blinde? In that (my lord quoth she) he was

maskt to poets memorie; and you know that falcons
against they flie, are hooded, to make them more fierce
and clearer sighted, and so perhaps was loue, which was
blindfold at first (in the opinion of Poets) who neuer
could see him rightly vntill they felt his eie in their
hearts. Why sticketh he his eie in their hearts? I had
thought (madam) it had beene his arrow said *Arsa-*
dachus. Why his eies are his arrowes, quoth the princesse,
(or I mistake his shooting;) for the last time he leuelled
at mee he hit me with a looke. I beshrew him (saide the
Prince) and then sounded the next measure, when *Arsa-*
dachus continued his discourse in this manner: Madam,
if loue wound by the eie, how healeth he? By the eie (my
lord said she) hauing the propertie of *Achilles* sword to
quell and recure. Then gracious lady quoth the prince,
since loue hath wounded mee by your lookes, let them
recouer mee, otherwise shall I blame both loues crueltie, and your iudgement. *Margarita* replied thus: Great
prince, if mine eies haue procured your offence, I will
plucke them out for their follie; and if loue haue shot
them for his shafts I beshrew him, for the last time they
lookt on you, they left my heart in you. In me mistris
quoth *Arsadachus*? Yea in you my lord quoth *Margarita*.
Can you then liue heartlesse (said the prince?) Yea since
hopelesse replied shee. This saide, the musicke cut off
their merry talke; and the sodaine disease of the Emperour brake vp the pastimes. Whervpon euery prince
and peere, lord and knight, taking leaue of their mis-
tresses, betooke them to their rest. Onely *Margarita*, in
whose bosome loue sate enthroned, in whose heart
affections kept their watch, being laide in her bed, fared
like *Orlando* sleeping in that bed his *Angelica* had lien
with *Medor*, each feather was a fur bush; now turned

he, now tossed she, now groueling on her face, now
olt vpright, hammering ten thousand fancies in her
head; at laſt, breaking out into a bitter sigh she beganne
hus: Alas vnkind loue, that seasoneſt thy delights with
lelaies. Why giueſt thou not poore ladies as great
atience to endure, as penance in their durance? why
re not thy affections like the figges of *India*, which are
oth grafted and greene of themselues, and no sooner
prung to a blossome, but spread in the bud? Why giu-
ſt thou Time swift wings to beginne thee, and so long
nd slowe ere hee seaze thee? I beseech thee loue, oh
ow she sighed when shee besought him! proine thou
he wings of Time, leſt he punish me, for thy delay is so
reat that my disease is vnsufferable: alas poore wretch
hat I am why prate, I to loue? or pray I for reliefe,
eing assured that the beginning of loues knowledge is
he ending of humane reason; loue is a passion that
nay not be expressed, conceiued beyond conceit, and
xtinguished beside cuſtome; ſtay thy minde therefore
oolish *Margarita*, for it beganne firſt in thee beyond
xpectation, and muſt end in thee beyond hope: for, as
here are no reasons but nature to prooue why the
wanne hateth the sparrow, the eagle the *Trochilus*, the
sse the bee, and the serpent the hogge; so likewise in
oue there can no cause but nature be alleadged either
f his sodaine flourish or vehement fall, his speedie
waxing and slow waining: Temper thy selfe therefore,
hough loue tempt thee, and waite thine oportunitie:
or the wanton if you fawne on him, will flie you; and
etting light by him, will leape vppon you. Fond that I
m, why talke I thus idlely, seeming with the prating
ouldiour to discourse of the fortresse I haue neuer con-
uered, and of the fancies I shall neuer compasse? Why

doth not *Arsadachus* smile on mee? as who knoweth not
that the aspis tickleth when she pricketh; and poisons
that are delightfull in the swallow, are deadly in the stom-
ach? why hath he not courted me these fiue moneths?
fond that I am, the more neare am I to my fall
for as the philosopher saith, men are like to the poison
of scorpions, for as the sting of the one killeth in three
dayes, so the pride and crueltie of the other quelleth a
kinde heart in lesse then a moment. Woe is me, I had
rather neede *Philoxenus* to cure me of loue by his laies,
then *Anippus* to continue loue in me: better were it for
me to heare *Tripander* play then *Arsadachus* preach.

In these thoughts and this speech loue sealed vp her
eies till on the morrow; but what she dreamed I leaue
that to you Ladies to decide, who hauing dallied with
loue, haue likewise beene acquainted with his dreames
On the morrow, the day being farre spent, and the
court replenished with attendants, *Margarita* arose, and
scarcely was shee attired, but that a messenger came
vnto her in the behalfe of the earle *Asaphus*, beseeching
her presence to grace his feast that day, for that he had
entertained and inuited *Arsadachus* and the best princes
and ladies in Court, by the Emperours consent, to make
a merry festiuall; whereunto *Margarita* quickly condes-
cended, and thought euery houre two till noonetide; a
which time roially attended, she repaired to *Asaphu*
house, where were assembled, of princes, *Arsadachus*
Plicorus, and *Stilconos*; of ladies, beside her selfe, *Calan
dra*, *Ephania*, and *Gerenia*: all these *Asaphus* entertained
heartily, placing them according to their degrees, and
feasted them with as great pompe and pleasure as he
could imagine.

But when he perceiued their appetites quelled with

delights, their eares cloyed with musicke, and their eies filled with beholding, he being a Prince of high spirit, began thus: Princes and Ladies, I haue inuited you to my house, not to entertaine you with the pompe of *Persia*, or the feaſt of *Heliogabalus*, but to dine you according to the directiõ of the phisitions, which is to let you rise with an appetite, which both whetteth your memories and helpeth your ſtomackes; and for that the after banket may as well please your humors, as the former appeased your hunger, I muſt beseeke you to rise frõ this place, and repaire vnto another, where because the weather is hot, and the time vnfit for exercise, we will spende the time in pleasant discourse, feeding our fancies with pleasant talke, as we haue feaſted our faſt with curious cates. To this motion all the assembly easily consented, in that for the moſt part, they had bin buzzing in their eares, and baiting their harts, whereupon he brought them into a faire arbor, couered with Roses, and honisuckles, paued with Camamile, pinkes, and violets, garded with two pretie chriſtall fountaines on euerie side, which made the place more coole, and the soyle more fruitfull. They all being entred this arbor, *Asaphus* being both learned and pleasant witted, began thus. My gheſts said he (for name of Princes I haue sent them lately vnto pallaces) now let each of you bethinke him of mirth not of maieſtie, I will haue no ſtoicall humor in this arbour, but all shall be either louers, or loues wel-willers, and for that, each of vs may bee more apt to talk of *Venus*; we wil taſte of her frend *Bacchus*; for a draught of good wine, (if *Lamprias* in *Plutarch*, may be beleeued) whettes the conceits, and he when he had drunke moſt, debated beſt: *Aschilus* therefore ere he had dipped his penne in the inke to write tragedies, diued into the bottome of a wine pot to find termes; for as, where the wolfe hath bitten moſt sound-eſt, the flesh is moſt sweeteſt, so wheras wine hath warmed moſt hotely, the tongue is armed moſt eloquently, I therefore carowse to you my familiars, and as I giue you licour to warme, so will I crowne you with ioy and roses to alay: then haue at loue who liſt, for me thinks I am alreadie prepared for him: This said he drunke vnto them, and all the reſt gave him the pledge, and being crowned after the manner of the philosophicall banquets, they sate downe. And *Arsadachus* spake thus: *Asaphus* I haue heard that the motion is vaine, vnlesse the action follow, and delights that are talked of before such as like them, except they grow in force, breede more discontent in their want, then pleasure in their report: as therefore you haue hanged out the Iuie bush, so bring forth the wine, as you haue prefixt the garland, so begin the race, as you intimated delight, so bring it to entrance. *Asaphus* smiling replied thus: Do then all these Ladies and braue louers giue me the honour and direction to gouern these sports? They do, said *Margarita*: Then sit aside quoth he and giue place to your commander; whereupon all the assembly laughed, and *Asaphus* smilingly sate downe in the high-eſt roome, placing the Ladies opposite againſt their louers, and himselfe seated in his soueraintie, began thus: Since in bankets the place is not to be giuen for the maieſtie, but the mirth, be not displeased though I preferre my selfe (my subiects,) since I know this, that I haue crothets in my head, when I haue taſted the cup, and no man is more apt to talke then I when I haue traffiked with good wine, and were it not so, you had no cause to waxe wroth with my presumption, for as the

mason preferreth not the attique ſtones in his building
for nobilitie, neither the painter his precious colours in
limning, for their liuelines, neither the shipwright his
Cretan cedar in framing for the sweetenesse: so in festiualles the gheſts are not to be placed, according to the
degrees, but their dispositions, for their liuelynesse, not
their liuelyhoods, for where pleasures are sought for,
the person is smally regarded, which considered, I am
iuſtified. But to our purpose, since loue is the affection
that leadeth vs, at him we will leuill our fancies, can-
uasing this queſtion amongſt vs, whether hee so beſt
worketh, by the eie, the touch, or the eare, for of the
fiue sences, I thinke these three are moſt forcible. Nowe
therefore wee will and command you, our masculine
subiects, said *Asaphus*, to beginne to our feminine Philosophers, and since you *Arsadachus* are of greateſt
hope, *incipe*. After they had all laughed heartily at the
maieſticall vtterance of *Asaphus*, and his imperious
manner, the yong Cuscan saide thus: The *Thebians* in
time paſt, who confined vpon *Pontus*, begat such children, who when they beheld their parents killed them
by their lookes, as it fared with them, so falleth it out
with me, who bethinking my selfe of those thoughtes,
which I haue conceiued in respect of loue, am con-
founded in thinking of them, such power hath fancie,
where it hath hold-faſt. I muſt therefore as they quelled
the one, kill the other, or I shall die by thoughts as they
did by lookes: but since to die for loue is no death but
delight, I will aduenture to thinke, talke, and discourse
of him, and rather perish my selfe, then suffer these pastimes to be vnperformed. Our queſtion is of loue faire
ladies, whereat you blush when I speake, and I bowe
when I thinke, for he giueth me words to discourse, and

courage to decide; for as *Plato* saith, loue is audacious in all things, and forward in attempting any thing: hee yeeldeth speech to the silent, and courage to the bashfull, hee giueth industrie to the negligent, and forwardnes to the sluggard, making a courtier of a clowne; and lighting on a currish *Minippus*, hee softeneth him as iron in the fire, and maketh him a courtly *Aristippus* vnder his safeconduct; therefore I will talke of him, and with your patience I will satisfie you, that loue hath soonest entrance by the eie, and greatest sustenance by the sight; for sight whereas it is stirred vp by many motions, with that spirit which it darteth out from it self, doth likewise disperse a certaine miraculous fierie force, by which meane we both doe and suffer many things: and as among all the senses, the eie extendeth his power furthest, so is his working most forcible; for as the clay petrot draweth fire, so the lookes do gather affection. And that the forcible working of the eie may be prooued to exceed all other the senses, what reason can be greater, since according to euery affection of the heart or distemperature of the minde, the radiations of the eie are correspondent; if the heart be enuious, the lookes dart out beames of fierce enuie, as may be considered by that of *Entelidas* in *Plutarch*:

Quondam pulcher erat crinibus Entelidas,
Sed sese ipse videns placidis in fluminis vndis:
Liuore infamis perdidit inuidiæ,
Facinus attraxit morbum, formamque perdidit.

For it is reported that this *Entelidas* taking a delight in his owne liuely beauty, and beholding the same in a spring, grew in enuy against the same; and by that

meanes fell into a sickenesse, whereby he lost both
health and beautie. *Narcissus*, neither by taste, nor the
ministerie of speech, nor the office of scent affected his
owne forme, but his sight bereft him of his senses, and
the eie drew fancie to the heart; for this cause the poets
call Ladies eies *Cupids* coach, the beames his arrowes;
placing all his triumph and power in them as the chiefest instrument of his seigniorie, and that the eie only
beside the ministerie of other senses, procureth loue,
you may perceiue by these examples following. *Xerxes*,
who despising the sea, and scorning the land found out
new meanes to nauigate, and armies to choake the
earth, yet fell in loue with a tree; for hauing seene a
plantane in *Lydia* of huge greatnesse, he staied vnder it
a hote day, making him a shelter of his shadow, a louer
of his loues; and afterwardes departing from the same,
he adorned it with collars of golde and iewelles, as if
that that tree had beene his enamoured, ouer which he
appointed a guardian to assist it, fearing lest any should
doe violence vnto the branches thereof. And what (I
pray you) moued this affection in *Xerxes* but the eie?
A noble yong man of *Athens* loued so much the stature
of good fortune erected neere vnto the *Prytaneum*, that
he embraced it, and kissed it, and offered a great summe
of money to the Senate to redeeme the same, and not
attaining his suite, hee slew himselfe; and what
wrought this in this noble yong man but the eie? for
his marble image had neither sent to delight the sent,
speach to affect the eare, nor other meanes to moue
affection; it was then the sole force of the eie which
conducteth to the heart each impression, and fixeth each
fancie in the same: what resteth there then but to giue
the honor to the eie? which as it is the best part in a

woman, so hath it the most force in loue. Soft (said
Plicotus) claime not the triumph before you heare th
triall; for if vertue and the whole praise thereof (as th
philosophers say) consisteth in act, let the touch hau
the first place, and the eie the second; for lookes do
but kindle the flame, where the touch both maketh i
burne, and when it listeth, quencheth the furie. Such a
beholde *Anter* are healed of the falling sickenesse (saiet)
Arsadachus) and they that sleepe vnder *Sinilan* at such
time as the plant swelleth and beareth his floure, ar
slaine. Quoth *Plicotus*, saffron floures procure sleepe
the Amethist staieth drunkennesse, by which reason
you ought to ascribe as much power to the scent as to
the sight. But heare me, you detracters from the touch
the hearb *Alissus* taken in the hand, driues sighes from
the heart. Yea but (said *Arsadachus*) the mad elephan
beholding the raine groweth wilde. Yea but the wilde
bull tied to the figge tree, and tasting thereof is no
more wrathful (said *Plicotus*) ascribe therefore to the
touch farre more then the sight; heape all the argumen
that can be for the eies, it breedeth the sickenesse: bu
wee rather commend the hearbe that purgeth the disease, then the humour that feedeth it, the salue tha
healeth the wound, than the corrosiue that grieueth it
the floure that comforteth the braine, and not tha
which cloyeth the same: the touch therefore in loue
should haue the prerogatiue which both reareth it, and
restraineth it; and that the touch hath greater powe
then the sight, what greater reason may be alleadged
then this, that we only see to desire, especially to touch
the furniture of all delight is the taste, and the purga
torie in loue, is to touch, and want power to execute the
affection, as may appeare by this example. In the daye

of *Apollonius Tiancus*, who by euery man was held for
the fountaine of wisedome, there was an eunuch found
out in *Babylon* who had vnlawfully conuersed with a
paramour of the Kings; for which cause the king demaunded of *Apollonius* what punishment the eunuch
ought to haue for that his rash and bold enterprise: no
other answered *Apollonius* saue that he liue to behold
and touch without further attempt. With which answere
the king being amazed, demaunded why he gaue this
answer. To whome *Apollonius* replied; Doubt not you,
O king, but that loue thall make him feele exceeding
paines and martirdomes; and like a simple flie, he shall
play so long with the flame vntill he fall to cinders. And
for further proofe the Egyptians (as *Ororius* reporteth)
when as they would represent loue do make a net: and
the *Phenitians* describe him in a hand laide in fire, ap-
prouing them by the touch which of all senses suffereth
most, and hath greatest power in the bodie. *Asaphus*
that was still all this while, sodainely brake off the discourse, saying thus: What sense (I pray you) was that
(ye philosophers) that perswaded *Ariston* of *Ephesus* to
lie with an asse, and to beget a daughter, which was
afterwards called *Onoselino*? what sense had *Tullius
Stellus* to be in loue with a mare, of whome he begat a
faire daughter which was called *Sponano*? what made
Cratis the Iloritane shepheard to loue a goate? *Pasiphæ*
to fancie a bull? *Stilconos* hearing that question, replied
thus: Truely a senslesse desire, which hauing no power
of loue but instinct of life, ought neither to be mentioned by modest tongues, nor vttered in chaste hearing: that loue which is gathered by the eie, and grounded in the heart, which springeth on the vniformitie of
affection, hauing in it selfe al the principles of musike

N

(as *Theophrastus* saith) as griefe, pleasure, and diuine
instruct that loue which the *Græcians* call *Ghiciprion*,
which is as much to say as bitter sweete; of that we
talke, and no other, which sacred affection I haue both
tasted with the eie, and tried by the touch, and haue
found so many effects in both, that as the sea ebbes and
flowes by the motion of the moone; the *Tropi* of Egypt
waxe and waine according to the flouds, and fall of
Nilus, so haue I by smiles, and louers pleasures, and
repulses, found such a taste in loue, that did not the
eare claim some greater preheminence, I should sub-
scribe to you both: but as loue beginneth by the sight,
and hath pleasure in the touch, so gathereth he his
eternitie from hearing, by hearing *Cupid* a boy, is made
Cupid a god, by hearing *Cupid* scarce fligd gathereth
store of feathers; for euen as breath extinguisheth fire
in the beginning, but when it is increased, both nourisheth and strengtheneth it, so loue that is couered in
embers by the aire, and scarce enabled and fashioned by
the touch, is angrie with those that discouer him; but
when he flies abroad, and braggeth in his wrings, he is
fedde with sweete wordes and laughes, at pleasant lan-
guish if he faint, kinde wordes do releeue him; if he be
sicke, perswasions purge him; if hee misdeeme, reasons
recouer him; in briefe, by the eare loue sucketh, by the
eare loue thriueth, and by the eare all his essence is
fashioned: and for that cause *Melpomene* and *Terpsicore*
the Muses are gouernours of our hearing, whereas not
any muse or godhead hath any affectiõ to the eie or
touch: for delight and gladnesse in loue proceedeth
from eloquent perswasion, which receiued by the eare
changeth, mooueth, altereth and gouerneth all the passions of the heart. *Margarita* blushing in that her turne
was next, draue *Stilconos* out of his text in this sort: My

lord (saide shee) if loue were gathered by the eare, olde
men for their wise discourses shoulde winne more
credite then yong men for their worthy comlines; or if
by the touch, loue had his triall, the diuinitie of loue
would be wronged by too much inhumanitie. It muſt
be the eie then which can discern the rude colt from the
trained ſteed, the true diamond from the counterfet
glasse, the right colour from the rude, and the perfect
beautie from the imperfect behauiour: had not the eie
the prerogatiue, loue shoulde bee a monſter, no myr-
acle: and were the touch only iudge, the soft Ermine
for daintinesse, the Seale for his softnesse, the Marterne
for his smoothe sweetenesse, would exceede both Ladies beſt perfections, and the fineſt skinne of the choic-
eſt louer. If by the eare loue were discerned, the Syren
by her sweet song should winne more fauour then
Sibilla for hir science, and the flatterer should be held
for the beſt fauourite: let the eie therfore haue the
preregatiue, which is both curious to beholde, and em-
perious to conquer. By it the heart may discouer his
affections as well as fine phrases, and more sweete hath
oftentimes beene gathered by a smile then a touch: for
by the one, we gather a hope of succeeding pleasure, by
the other, a ioy in suspect for feare we be deceiued,
which beginneth in a minute and endeth in a moment.
All cattes are grey in the darke (said *Calandra*) and
therefore (good madam) you doe well to preferre the
eie. Yea but said *Ephania*, the eie had neede of a candle
to light it, or else (perhaps) the fatte were in the fire.
Well (said *Gerenia*) I will truſt mine eare then: for
where neither the eie seeth, nor the touch feeleth, cer-
tainely by darke let me heare the words, for they are the
tell-troths. Ah *Gerenia* (said *Stilconos*) truſt them not,
or they that are false for the moſt part by day, wil

(perhappes) faile you in the night. Leaue your talke (quoth *Asaphus*) and shut mee all these three sences in one, and then tell me the felicitie; when the eie shall giue earnest of the heart, the heart take comfort by the eare, the wordes we haue heard, and the sights wee haue seene confirmed by touch, this is the loue I had rather haue in mine armes then heare it in this place discoursed by argument. Since therefore (my subiects) you are at my obeisance, and vpon my direction are to doe homage to loue, I giue you free licence to discourse, free libertie to looke, the sweetes whereof, after you haue gathered, come to me, and after the priest hath hand-fasted you, come touch and spare not, you shall haue my pattent to take your pleasure. It is a dangerous matter (said *Arsadachus*) to enter those lists where women will do what they list. Wel (saide *Margarita*) diuels are not so blacke as they be painted (my Lorde) nor women so wayward as they seeme. A good earnest peny (quoth *Asaphus*) if you like the assurance. With that they brake vp the assembly, for it was supper time, and the prince intreated them to sit downe, where they merrily passed the time, laughing heartily at the pleas- ant and honest mirth wherein they had passed that afternoone.

The supper ended, each louer tooke his mistres apart, where they handled the matter in such sort, that *Mar- garita* which was before but easily fired, now at last grew altogether inflamed, for the night calling them thence, and the companie taking their leaue, she with a bitter sigh and earnest blush, tooke her leaue of *Arsa- dachus* thus: My Lord said she, if time lost bee hardly recouered, and fauours wonne are to be followed, haue a care of your estate, who may bragge of that fortune

that no one in *Mosco* can equall: which saide, she in all
her periode of sighes ending as abruptly as she had
begun, and so departed. *Arsadachus* that knew the tree
by the fruit, the cloth by the list, the apple by the tast,
fained not to see what he most perceiued, and taking
his leaue of *Asaphus* departed to his lodging where in a
carelesse vaine, as if cloking and smothering with loue,
he wrote these verses,

Iudge not my thoughts, ne measure my desires,
  By outward conduct of my searching eies,
For starres resemble flames, yet are no fires:
  If vnder gold a secret poison lies,
If vnder softest flowers lie Serpents fell,
  If from mans spine bone Vipers do arise,
So may sweete lookes conceale a secret hell,
  Not loue in me, that neuer may suffice
The heart that hath the rules of reason knowne,
  But loue in me which no man can deuise,
A loue of that I want, and is mine owne,
  Yet loue, and louers lawes do I despise:
How strange is this? iudge you that louers be,
  To loue, yet haue no loue conceald in me.

And other he wrote in this manner, which came to
the hands of his mistris, who prettilie replied; both
which I haue vnderwritten.

I smile to see the toies,
  Which I in silent see,
The hopes, the secret ioyes,
  Expected are from me:
The vowes, the sighes, the teares, are lost in vaine,
  By silly loue through sorrow welnie slaine.

The colour goes and comes,
  The face, now pale, now red,
Now feare the heart benomes,
  And hope growes almoſt dead.
And I looke on and laugh, tho sad I seeme,
  And faine to fawne altho my minde misdeeme.

I let the flie disport,
  About the burning light,
And feede her with resort,
  And baite her with delight.
But when the flames hath seasd her winges (adew)
  Away will I, and seeke for pleasures new.

Smile not, they are no toyes,
  Which you in silent see.
Nor hopes, nor secret ioyes,
  Which you beholde in mee:
But those my vowes, sighes, teares, are serious seales,
  Whereby my heart his inward griefe reueales.

My colour goes and comes,
  My face is pale and red,
And feare my heart benomes,
  And hope is almoſt dead:
And why? to see thee laugh at my desart
  So faire a man, and yet so false a heart.

Well, let the flie disport,
  And turne her in the light:
And as thou doſt report,
  Still baite her with dispite:
Yet be thou sure, when thou haſt slaine the furſt,
  Thou flieſt away (perhaps) to find the worſt.

Thus passed the affaires in *Mosco* til such time as the emperour growing more and more in sicknes; by the consent of his nobles, hasted on the marriage. The rumor whereof being spread abroad, made euery one reioice; but among the rest, *Margarita* triumphed, who called into open assembly by the Emperour, was betrothed to *Arsadachus* in the presence of the nobilitie, who by his lowring lookes at that time, shewed his discontents; yet will he, nill he, the day was appointed, the sixteenth of the Calends of *March*, next insuing: against which time there were high preparations in Court, and throughout all the prouinces for pastimes. But since it is a most true axiome among the Philosophers, that whereas be many errors, there likewise must needs follow many offences: it must needly follow, that since *Arsadachus* was so fraught with corrupt thought, hee should practise and performe no lesse vngratious corrupt and vngodly actions, for no sooner was hee departed from the presence of the Emperour, but he presently beganne to imagine how to breake off his nuptialls, forcing in himselfe a forgetfulnesse of *Margaritaes* vertues, her loue and good deserts, so that it may euidently be perceiued and approued that which *Ammonius* saith, that things concluded in necessitie are dissolued by violence, and truely not without reason was loue compared to the sunne, for as the sun thrusteth forth his purer and warmer beams through darknes and the thickest cloude, so loue pierceth the most indurate heartes, and as the sunne is sometime inflamed, so likewise is vnstable loue quicklie kindled. Moreouer, as the constitution of that body which vseth no exercise endureth not the sunne, so likewise an illiterate and corrupt mind cannot entertaine loue, for both of them after the same manner are disturbed from their estates, and attainted with sicknes, blaming not the force of loue, but their owne weakenesse. But this difference is betweene loue and the sunne, for that the sunne sheweth both faire and foule things to those that looke on vpon the earth: loue onelie taketh care of the beautie of faire things, and onely fixeth the eies vpon such things, enforcing vs to let slip all other. By this may be gathered that *Arsadachus* being vicious coulde not iustly be attainted with loue, but with some slight passion, such as affect the greatest tyrants in beholding the pittifull massacre of the innocent, as shal manifestly appeare by the sequele: for after long debating in his restlesse minde, somtime to flie the court, and by that meanes to escape the bondage which he supposed was in wedlocke; sometime to make the princes away by poison, ridding himselfe thereby of suspect, and *Artosogon* of hope. Fortune is as well the patronesse of iuiuries, as the protector of iustice, the scourge of the innocent, as the fauourer of the nocent, who is rightly blind in hauing no choice, and worthily held for bedlam, in that she respecteth no deserts, so smiled on him that in depth of his doubts a remedy was ministred him beyond his imagination, which fell out after this maner. *Artosogon* his father being so tired with yeares, as he must of force yeeld speedie tribute to death; so loaden with sickenesse that he seemed welnie past all succours, bethinking him of his succession, and like a kind father, desirous (before his death) to beholde his sonne, not without the earnest entreaty of the empresse, and his nobility, sent present messengers to *Mosco*, beseeching the emperour *Protomachus* presently to dispatch *Arsadachus* vnto him, assuring him of the perilous estate of his life, and the desire he had to ſtablish his son before his death: for wherfore the emperour of *Mosco* (though loathly) dismissed his pretended triumphs, and gaue *Arsadachus* licence to depart for *Cusco*.

The vngodly yong prince seeing his purposes fall out so happily, sacrificed to *Nemesis*, cleering his browes of those cares wherewith discontent had fraught them: and hauing with all expedition furnished himselfe to depart, hee thought good to caſt a faire foile on his false heart, to colour his corrupt thoughts with comfortlesse throbbes; and comming to *Margarita*, (who was almoſt dead to heare the tidings) with a fained look and false heart he thus attempted her. Madam were I not assiſted with my sighes, and succored by my teares, to disburthen the torments of my heart, I feare me it shoulde euen now burſt, it is so fraught with bitternesse, Alas I muſt now leaue you, being the bark to the tree, the blossome to the ſtalk, the sent to the flower, the life to the bodie, the subſtance to the shadow; I muſt now leaue you being the beutiful whom I honor, the chaſt whom I adore, and the goddesse of al my glorie; I muſt now leaue you to liue in sorrow without comfort, in dispaire without solace, in tears without rescouse, in pains without ceasing; I muſt now leaue you as the dam her yong kid, the ew her deare lambkin, the nightingale her prettieſt neſtling, fearing leſt the cuckow hatch those chickens which I haue bred, the *Callax* bring vp those yong fish I haue got, and forren eies feed on those beuties which only faſten life in me: Ah *Margarita*, so faire, as none so faire, more vertuous then vertue her selfe; if these troubles attaint me, in what temper shal I leaue you, being the mirror of beauty, and euen the miracle of conſtancie? me thinkes I see those iniurious,

though faire hands, beating those delicate brests, these
eies surffeting with tears, these lips with blasting their
roses with sighings: but (ah deere lady) let not such
follies be your familiars; for as the thorne pricking the
dead image in waxe pierceth the liuely substance indeede, so euerie light filip you giue this breast, will fell
this bodie, euery light teare that trickleth from these
eies, wil melt me to water, the least sighs steaming frō
these lippes, will stifle me, haue therefore patience
(sweete ladie) and gouerne your passions with discretion; for as the smallest kernell (in time) maketh the
tallest tree; so (in time) these shadowes of sorrow shall
turne to the substance of delight: yea in short time my
returne shall make you more happy then my present
departe nowe maketh you heauy. With these words
Arsadachus was ready to take his leaue. When *Margarita* presaging the mischiefe that was to follow; casting her armes about his necke, gaue him this sorrowfull
adue.

Since my misgiuing mind assureth me of my succeeding harme: ah suffer me (sweet prince) to embrace
that which I neuer heereafter shall beholde and looke
vpon; that with my weeping eies which is the cause of
all my wastefull enuies: Ah my soule, must thou leaue
me when wert wholy incorporate in this bodie? Ah my
heart, must thou forsake mee to harbour in this happy
bosome? What then shall remaine with me to keep me
in life, but my sorow? being the bequest of misery shal
assist me in my melancholy: ah deare *Arsadachus* since
thou must leaue me, remember thou leauest me without
soule, remember thou leauest me heartlesse: yea I
woulde to the gods thou mightst leaue me lifelesse, for
then disburthened of this body, I might in soule accom-

panie thee, vniting our partes of fire: since our fleshly persons must be parted, farewell (deare Lord) farewell, euer deare Lord, but I beseech thee, not for euer (deare Lord) remember thou hast conquered, and art to triumph, thou hast gotten the goale, and art to reape the garland; thou hast taken the captiue, and maiest enioy the ransome: hie thee therefore, oh hie thee lest heauinesse ouerbeare me; returne to her that shall liue in terrour till thou returne. But if some angrie fates, some vntowarde fortune, some sinister planet detaine thee, and with thee, my soule, heart, life and loue; now now, oh now ye destinies, end me. This said, she fell in a swowne, and her Ladies coulde hardly recouer life in her. Meane while (by the direction of the emperour) who heard her impatience, *Arsadachus* was called away, to whom *Protomachus* presented many gifts, swearing him in solemne manner before the whole assembly of his nobilitie, to make a speedy returne to Mosco, to accomplish the marriage. In the meane time *Margarita* was reuiued, who seeing her *Arsadachus* absent, demeaned her selfe in the most pitifull manner that euer poore lamentable Ladie did: at last remembring her of a rich iewell which *Arsinous* had given her, which was a pretious box set with emeraulds, the which at such time as he gaue it her, hee charged her to keepe vntill such time as he she loued best should depart from her; she sent the same for a present to *Arsadachus*, beseeching him as he loued her, neuer to open the same boxe vntill such time as he beganne in any sort to forget her (for such counsell *Arsinous* had giuen her.) This present was deliuered the prince when he mounted on horse, who promised carefully to keepe it; and with his retinue rode on his way towards Cusco: where we leaue him to

returne to *Margarita*, who no sooner heard of the departure of *Arsadachus*, but laying apart her costly iewels,
her rich raiment, and princely pleasures, closed herself
vp in a melancholy tower, which through the huge
height thereof beheld the countrey farre and neere: on
the top whereof, each houre she diligently watched for
the returne of her beloued *Arsadachus*. Her lodging
was hangd about with a cloth of black veluet embrodered about with dispaires; before her bed hung the
picture of her beloued: to which she often discoursed
her vnkindnesse conceiued, offering drops of her blood
daily to the deafe image; such a fondling is loue, when
he groweth too fierie, no day, no night passed her,
wherein she spent not many houres in teares, and many
teares euery houre, neither could the authoritie of her
father, the perswasions of his counsaile, nor the intreat-
ings of her attendants, alter her resolution.

In which melancholie a while I will leaue her to discourse the damned treasons of *Arsadachus*, who arriuing
at last in Cusco, after long iourneis was after many
hearty welcomes conducted to his father, who receiued
such sodaine ioy at the sight of him, that he recouered
strength, and cast off his sickenesse; so that calling his
nobilitie vnto him, hee ordained a time wherein *Arsadachus* should be inuested in the empire, publishing the
same through al his prouinces. In the meane time with
much mirth and festiuall, the yoong Prince liued in his
fathers court, deerely tendered by the empresse *Lelia*
his mother, and duely attended by the best of the nobilitie, among whom *Argias* the duke of *Morauia*, being
a prince of deepe reach, and of great reuenues, following the custome of such who desire to grow in fauour
with Princes, entertained *Arsadachus* with huge feasts

and bankets: and among the rest, with one most especiall, wherein as he had imployed al whatsoeuer the
country could afford to delight the tast, so spared he no
cost to breede pastime and triumph. Among all other,
after the supper was solemnized, he brought in a maske
of the goddesses, wherein his daughter (being the mir-
rour and the *Aperse* of the whole world for beautie) was
apparelled like *Diana,* her haire scattered about her
shoulders, compassed with a siluer crownet, her necke
decked with carkanets of pearle, her daintie body was
couered with a vaile of white net-work wrought with
wiers of siluer, and set with pearle, where through the
milke white beauties of the sweete Saint gaue so heauenly a reflexion, that it was sufficient to make *Saturne*
merry and mad with loue, to fixe his eie on them: among
all the rest that had both their partes of perfection and
beautie, and great louers to like thẽ, *Arsadachus* made
choise of this *Diana* (who not onely resembled her in
that shew, but indeed was called by the name of *Diana*)
on whose face when he had fixed his eies, he grew so
inflamed as *Montgibel* yeeldeth not so much smoke as he
sent out sighes: to be briefe, he grew so sodainely altered, that as such as beheld the head of *Medus* were
altred from their shapes, so he that saw the heauen of
these beauties, was rauished from his sences: to bee
briefe, after he had danced the measures, passed the
night, and was conducted by *Argias* and his attendants,
hee tooke no rest, but tossing on his bed, grew so
altered, that on the morrow all the court was amazed to
behold his melancholies. It cannot be reported how
strangely he demeaned himselfe, for his sleeps fled him,
his colour changed, his speech vncertain, his apparel
carelesse: which *Argias* perceiuing as being maruellous

pollitique, ministred oile to the lamp, fuel to the fire, flaxe to the flame, encreasing his daughters beautie with cost, and *Arsadachus* loue by her companie; for he ceased not to inuite him, hoping that at the last the cloudes would breake out and raine him some good fortune. *Diana* was trained by him to the lewre, and taught her lesson with great cunning, who was as apt to execute as her father to counsell. *Arsadachus* one day among the rest finding the opportunitie, and desirous to discouer his conceits was stricken so dombe with her diuine beautie, as he could not disclose his minde. Whereupon calling for pen and inke, he wrote this, thrusting it in *Dianaes* bosome, walked melancholy into a faire garden on the backe side of *Argiaes* pallace, where he wept so bitterly, that it was supposed his heart would burst.

I pine away expecting of the houre,
  Which through my waiward chance will not arriue,
I waite the word, by whose sweete sacred power,
  My lost contents may soone be made aliue:
My pensiue heart, for feare my griefe should perish,
  Vpon fallacious hope his fast appeaseth;
And to my selfe my frustrete thoughts to cherish,
  I faine a good that flits before it ceaseth:
And as the ship farre scattered from the port,
  All welnie spent and wreckt with wretched blast,
From East to West, midst surging seas is tossed,
  So I, whose soule by fierce delaies effort,
Is ouercome in heart and lookes desast,
  Runne heere, runne there, sigh, die, by sorrow crossed.

Diana tooke no daies to peruse this ditty, but hauing ouerread it, gaue it her father to iudge of, who faining

a seueritie more then ordinarie, and glad of the opportunitie, entered the garden where the prince was welnie
forespent with sorrow, and taking occasion to interrupt
his meditations, he began thus: Moſt royall Prince, I
thinke the heauens lowre on me, that labouring by al
indeuours to procure your delights, I rather find you
more melancholy by my motions, then merry by my
entertainment: Alas my Lord, if either my actions do
displease, my entertainement bee too bace, or if in anie
thing I haue defaulted, wherein I may make amends, I
beseech you let me know of you, and you shall finde
such readines in me, your humble seruant, as no hasard,
danger, or discommoditie whatsoeuer, shall driue me
from the accomplishment of your pleasures and beheſts.
Arsadachus seeing *Argias* so plyant beganne to recouer
hope, whereupon fixing his eies vpon him a long while,
at laſt he brake his mute silence thus: *Argias*, thy curtesie can not boade my discontents, for thy kindenesse
is such as bindes me vnto thee, and breeds me no
melancholie; and for I see thee so careful for my good,
I will firſt therefore shew thee of what important, secrecie is, and declare vnto thee, those punishments
antiquitie beſtowed on those that reuealed secrets.
Laſtly vpon thy faithfull oth I may ventre further, but
so as thy silence may make thee happieſt man in *Cosco*.
To be of faire words (*Argias*) becommeth a man of
much vertue; and no small treasure findeth that Prince
who hath a priuy and faithful secretarie, in whose
bosome he may powre his thoughts, on whose wisedome
hee may repose his secrets. *Plutarch* writeth that the
Athenians hauing warre with king *Philip* of *Macedon*,
by chaunce lighted vpon certaine letters which he had
written to *Olimpias* his wife, which they not onely sent

backe sealed and vnsearched, but also said, that since
they were bound by their laws to be secret, they would
neither see nor reade other mĕs priuate motions, *Dio-
dorus Siculus,* writeth that among the *Egyptians* it was
a criminal act, to open secrets which he proueth to be
true, by example of a priest, who had vnlawfull companie with a virgin of the goddesse *Isis,* both which
trusting their secrecie to another priest, and hee hauing
little care to keepe their action concealed, sodainely
cried out, where through the offenders were found out
and slaine, and he banished. And where as the same
priest complained against the vniust sentence, saying:
that whatsoeuer he had reueled was in fauour of relig-
ion, he was answered by the Iudge, if thou alone hadst
knowne it without being priuie to them, or hadst thou
had notice without corrupt consent, thou shouldst haue
reason to be aggreeued; but sodainely whereas they
trusted their secrecie vnto thee which they had in hand,
and thou promisedst them to keepe silence, hadst thou
remembred thee of thy bond and promise, and the law
which we haue to be secret in all things, thou hadst
neuer had the courage to publish it. *Plutarch* in his
booke of banishment saith, that an *Athenian* sought
vnder the cloke of an *Egyptian,* asked him what hee
carried hid, to whom he answered: Thou shewest thy
selfe smally read and worse nurtured (O thou *Athenian*)
sith thou perceiuest not that I carrie this hid for no
other respect, but that I would haue no man know what
I carrie, many other are the examples of *Anaxileus,
Dionisius, Plato,* and *Bias,* which were too long for me
to report, and too tedious for thee to heare, my onely
desire is to let thee knowe the waight of secrecie, and
the punishment that knowing the one and the other

(my *Argias*) thou mightſt in respect of thy life keepe silence with the tongue.

Argias that knew the bird by the feather, and the eagle by the flight, the leopard by his spot, and the lyon by his claw, cut off his circumlocutions, with this discourse; *Ariſtarchus* the Philosopher (moſt noble prince) was wont to say, that by reason of their inſtabilitie, knew not that which the moſt men ought to desire, nor that which they should flie, because that euerie day changeth, and swift Time flieth: *Eubeus* the Philosopher, was wont many times to talke this at the table of great *Alexander*; by nature euerie one is prompt and sharpe witted, to giue counsell and to speake his opinion in other mens affaires, and fond and slow in his owne purposes. Truely this sentence was both graue and learned, for manie there be that are discreet in other mens causes, and iudge rightly, but among ten thousand there is not one that is not deceiued in his own causes. This considered, your grace doth moſt wisely, to seeke to disburden your thoughts in a secret bosome, and to aske counsell of another in your earneſt occasions, for by the one you shall benefite your griefe, by the other conquer it. Hiſtories report that the valiant captaine *Nicias*, was neuer miſtaken in any thing which atchiued by another mans counsell, neither euer brought any thing to good effect, which he managed according to his owne opinion. It is therefore vertue in you (good prince) if in immitation of so great a Chiefetaine, you rather truſt other mens wisedome, then your owne wit: and since it pleaseth you to grace me with the hope of secrecie, your excellencie shall not to neede to misdoubt, for by all those gods whom I reuerence, by this right hand which I lay on thy honourable loines, so

o

may my pastures be plentifull, my barnes filled, my
vines burthened, as I vow to be secret, resolued to seale
my faith with such assurance, as death it self shal neuer
be able to dissolue it. *Arsadachus* hearing his zealous
promises, and weighing his wise answeres, by the one,
assured himselfe of his loyaltie, by the other, gathered
his great wisedome and learning; whereupon taking
Argias by the hand, and withdrawing himselfe into a
verie secrete and cloose arbour in the garden, hee, after
hee had a while rested himselfe, and meditated on that
he had to say, with a bitter sigh brake out into these
speeches. Oh *Argias*, had the destinies made vs as prone
to indure the assaults of loue, as they haue made vs
prompt to delight in them, if they had fauoured vs with
as much power to pacifie the furie of them, as they haue
giuen vs will to persever in the follie, I could then be
mine owne phisition, without discouering my griefe,
and salue that with discretion, which I nowe sigh for
through dispaire. But since they haue denied vs that
grace in their secret wisedome, to haue wil to relieue
our own weaknesse, purges to expulse our poysons, and
constancie to endure loues conflicts, I must haue re-
course vnto thee, in whom cõsisteth the source of all my
safetie, beseeching thee (deare *Argias*) if thou hearest
that thou shouldest not, consider that I suffer that I
would not, and so temper my defects, by the force and
effects of thy wisedome, that I may be relieued and thou
nothing greeued. Thou knowest sweet friend the contract I haue past with *Margarita*, thou knowest the resolution of my father wholly bent to accomplish it, thou
knowest the expedition is required to accomplish the
mariage: al which shall no sooner be accomplished, but
I shall perish, and that day I shall become the bride-

grome of *Margarita*, I wish to be buried in my graue:
this is the firſt mischiefe muſt be anticipated, this the
firſt sore muſt be salued, this the firſt consumption
muſt haue a cordiall: Mightie prince said *Argias*, those
conditions that consiſt on impossibilities may be broken, and marriage which by an inviolable law of nature
was ordained to knit and vnite soules and bodies to-
gither, cannot be rightly solemnised betweene such,
whose good likings haue not the same limits, whose
affections are not vnited with selfe like faculties, for as
to ioyne fire and water, moiſt and drie, were a matter
impossible, especially in one subiect, and more, in that
they be contraries; so to couple loue where there is
hatred, affinitie where there is no fancie, is a matter
againſt right, repugnant to reason, and such a thing as
since nature doth impugne it, the gods if it be broken
will easilie dispence withall, whereas therefore you are
a prince in your waxing yeares, your father in his waining, in your pride of wit; your father is impouerished in
his vnderſtanding; since the cause concerneth you in
act, him but in words, since this domage is but the
breach of a silly vowe, if the marriage be broke, your
detriment the miserie of an age without all manner of
content, you may (good prince) in reason to preuent
your owne harm in iuſtice, since you cannot affect,
break off those bands: and if *Protomachus* shall threaten,
let him play the woulfe and barke againſt the sun, hee
cannot bite: you haue power to resiſt him, and friends
to assiſt you, I but my father (*Argias*) how shal we
pacifie him? either by perswasions (good prince) said
Argias, or by inpulsiõ, by the laws of *Solon*, old men
that dote muſt be gouerned by yong men that haue discretion, if he gainsay you there are meanes to temper

him, better he smart then you perish, my shirt is neare
me my Lord, but my skin is nearest, the cause concerneth you and must not be dallied. *Arsadachus* hauing
found a hauke fit for his own lure, and a counseller
agreeable to his owne conceit, with a smiling regard he
greeted *Argias* againe in this kind of manner: deere
friend, thou hast rid me of my doubtes, and wert onely
reserued me by the gods, to redresse my domage. Thou
haste complotted the means to displace *Margarita*, to
appease *Artosogon*, now if to pacifie that raging affection
that subdueth me, thou find me a remedie, I wil make
thee the chiefest man in *Cusco*, of most authoritie in
court; yea thou shalt bee my second hart (my *Argias*)
and yet this which I require of thee though it be the
difficultest in me, is the easiest in thee; for if it be lawfull for me as thou prouest, to breake my first marriage,
to bridle my father, and worke also whatso is mine own
will, what letteth my second wedlocke with which thy
fauor shall be solemnised betweene thy angelicall *Diana*
and me, wherethrough I shall haue peace, and thou
preheminence? *Argias* that had alreadie caught the foxe
in the snare, now laide hands of him, and with a pleasing countenance beganne thus. O Prince this last doubt
is your least daunger, for where you may command my
life, where you are lord of my wealth, can I be so forget-
full of duetie, thinke you to denie you my daughter,
whose worth is of too great weakenesse, to entertaine
such dignitie? but since it pleaseth your excellence to
daine it her in vertuous sort, command me and her to
our vtmost powers, we are yours. *Arsadachus* thinking
himselfe in heauen, thanked *Argias* for his courtesie, who
at last wholly discouered vnto him, how secret he was
to his affections, shewing him his sonnet: to be briefe,

it was so complotted that without further delay, *Arsa-dachus* should bee presently wedded to *Diana*, which was effected so, that both these two married couples in the height of their pleasures, passed their time in won-derfull delight in *Argias* castle. But as nothing is hidden from the eie of Time, neither is any thing so secret which shall not be reuealed: the emperor *Artosogon* (by reason of *Arsadachus* continuall abode at *Argias* house) discouered at last both the cause and the contract: whereupon, storming like the Ocean incensed with a north-east brise, he presently sent for *Argias*; and with-out either hearing his excuses, or regard of his intreat-ies, presently caused him to be torne in peeces at the tailes of foure wilde horses, then casting his mangled members into a litter, hee sent them to *Diana* in a pre-sent, vowing to serue her in the same sawce her father had tasted, that durst so insolently aduenture to espouse with the sole heire of his empire. The poore ladie almost dead, to see the dead bodie of her father, but more moued with her owne destruction which was to follow, fell at *Arsadachus* feete, beseeching him with brinish teares, which fell in her delicate bosome, to be the patrone of her fortunes. *Arsadachus* who loued her en-tirely, comforted her the best he might, assuring her safetie, in spight of his fathers tyrannie; whereuppon he leuied a guard of his chiefest friends to the number of three thousand men, and shutting *Diana* in a strong fortresse, left her after many sweet embraces in their custodie: and for that the time of his coronation drew neere, he assembled foure thousand such as hee knew most assured; he repaired to the court, vowing in his mind such a reuenge on his father, as all the world should wonder to heare the sequele. Being arriued in

court, hee cloyed the gates thereof with armed men,
placing in euery turning of the citie sufficient rowts of
guard to keepe the citizens from insurrection: Then
ascending the royall chamber where the Emperour his
father with his nobilitie were resident, hee prowdly
drew him from his seate royall; in which action those of
the nobilitie which resisted him were slaine, the rest
that tremblingly behelde the tragedie, heard this which
ensueth: *Arsadachus* prowdly setting him in his fathers
seate, was ready to speake vnto the assembly, when the
olde Emperour that had recouered his fall, awaking his
spirites, long dulled with age and weakenesse, beganne
in this sort to vpbraide his vngracious heire: Viper
villaine and worse, auaunt, and get thee out of my presence. How darest thou lay handes on thy Lord? or staine
the emperiall seate with thine impure and defiled person? Canst thou behold thy father without blushes,
whom thou hast periured by thy peruersenesse, making
my othes frustrate through thine odious follies? ah
caitife as thou art! more depraued then *Caligula*, more
bloudy indeed then *Nero*, more licentious then *Catuline*:
would God either thou hadst beene vnborne, or better
taught. Thou second *Tarquine* fostered by me to worke
tragedies in *Cusco*: thou prowd yongman, thy beauty
thou hast employed in riot, thy forces in tyranny: Oh
vnkind wretch, I see, I see with mine eies the subuersion of this Empire, and that which I haue kept fourtie
yeeres, thou wilt loose in lesse then thirtie moneths.
How can thy subiects be obedient to thee that despisest
thy father? How can these Nobles hope for iustice at
thy hands, that hast iniuriously attempted mee, an olde
man, thy father, that bred thee, thy lord, that cherished

thee, the emperour that muſt inherite thee. What may
ſtrangers truſt in thee, that haſt broken thy faith with
Protomachus, abused the loue of *Margarita*, and all for a
faire faced minion, whom if I catch in my clawes I will
so temper as thou shalt haue little luſt to triumph? O
what pittie is it thou peruerse man, to see how I haue
bought thee of the gods with sighes; how thy mother
hath deliuered thee with paine; how we both haue
nourished thee with trauelles; how we watched to sus-
taine thee; how we laboured to releeue thee; and after,
how thou rebelleſt, and art so vicious, that wee thy
miserable parents muſt not die for age, but for the
griefe wherewith thou doeſt torment vs? Ah woe wo is
me that beholdeth thy lewdnesse, and wretched art thou
to follow it: well did I hope that thy courage in armes,
thy comelinesse in person, thy knowledge in letters
were vertues enow to yeelde me hope, and subdue thy
follies: but now I say and say againe, I affirme and
affirme againe, I sweare and sweare againe, that if men
which are adorned with natural gifts do want requisit
vertues, such haue a knife in their hands wherewith
they do ſtrike and wound themselues, a fire on their
shoulders wherewith they burne themselues, a rope on
their necks to hang themselues, a dagger at their breaſts
to ſtab themselues, a ſtone to ſtumble at, a hill to tum-
ble downe. Ah would to God that members wanted in
thee, so that vice did not abound: or woulde the losse of
thine eies might recompence the lewdnes of thine er-
rours. But thou laugheſt to heare me lament, which
sheweth the small hope of amends, thou haſt no touch
of conscience, no feare of the gods, no awe of thy
parents, what then should I hope of thee? would God
thy death, for that were an end of detriment: if thy life,

I beseech the gods for mine own sake close mine eies by death, lest I see thy vniust dealings.

In this state *Arsadachus* that was resolued in his villany without any reply (as if scorning the old man) caused his tong by a minister to be cut out, then commaunded his right hand to be strooke off, wherewith he had signed the writ of *Argias* death; afterwards apparelling him in a fooles coate, and fetching a vehement laughter, he spake thus: *Cuscans*, wonder not, it is no seueritie I shew, but iustice; for it is as lawfull for me to forget I am a sonne, as for him to forget he is a father; his tongue hath wronged me, and I am reuenged on his tongue, his hand hath signed to the death of my deere *Argias*, and it hath payed the penaltie: and since the old man doateth, I haue apparelled him according to his propertie and impatience, wishing all those that loue their liues, not to crosse mee in my reuenges, nor assist him in his sinister practises. This saide, he made all the nobilitie to sweare loyaltie vnto him; and *Diana* laughing incessantly at the old man, who continual pointed with his left hand, and lifted his eies to heauen for reuenge, sometimes he imbraced the nobles, inciting them by signes to reuenge, but all was in vaine, scare subdued their affections.

In the meane while, the newes of these nouelties were spread throw the citie, so that many tooke armes to reuenge the old emperour, who were presently and incontinently slain by the souldiers: in briefe, as in all conflicts, the weake at last went to the wall, and necessitie inforced such as misdeemed of *Arsadachus* proceedings, to allow of them in shew: the day of coronation drew on, against which time *Lelia* the Empresse (little suspecting that which had fallen out) arriued in *Cusco*,

who hearing of the hard measure was offered her husband by her vngratious sonne (for *Artosogon* was shut vp
all the day till meale times, when *Arsadachus* called for
him foorth to laugh at him) she entred the pallace with
such cries, as might haue made the hardeſt heart melt
to heare them, where clasping of her armes about the
necke of the olde and aged man, who melted in teares
to behold the melancholy of the chaſte matron, she
cried out and complained in this manner: O you iuſt
gods; can you see these wrongs without remedie? are
you deafe to heare, or pittilesse to redresse? Ah, looke
downe looke downe from your thrones, and behold my
throbbes, witnes such wrongs as the sunne hath neuer
seene the like; the dogge is gratefull to his maiſter for
his meate, the elephant to his teacher for his knowledge,
the serpent to the hunts man for his life; but our vntoward sonne, for releeuing him, hath grieued vs, for
giuing him sweete milke in his youth, doth feede vs
with bitter aloes in our age; and I for bearing him with
many groanes, am now betraied by him to many griefes:
Ah *Artosogon*, ah my deere *Artosogon*, it is enough griefe
for thee to indure, let me weep (for the old man, to see
her, shed many teares) because thou sufferest, that as
thou decayeſt through tyrany, I may die with teares.
This said, sorrow ſtopped the passage of her speech,
and they both swowned, hee to beholde his *Lelia* so
forlorne, she to see her *Artosogon* so martyred: he that
saw *Venus* lamenting *Adonis*, *Aurora* bewailing *Memnon*,
Mirrha her tosſt fortunes, saw but the shadow of cares,
not the subſtance of complaints; for this sorrowe of the
princes was onely beyond compare, and paſt beleefe;
wherein so long they demeaned themselues, till age and
sorrow, after long ſtrife surrendred to death, who pit-

tied the olde princes, being despised of their lewd sonne, and ended their sorrowes in ending them. The rumour of whose fall was no sooner bruited in the eares of *Arsadachus*, but that instead of solemnizing their funeralles, he frequented his follies, instead of lamenting for them, hee laughed at them, causing them for fashion sake to haue the fauour of the graue, not for any fauour he bare them: then calling for *Diana* to his court, he honoured her as a goddesse, causing his subiects to erect a shrine, and to sacrifice vnto her: and such was his superstitious and besotted blindnes, that he thought it the only paradise of the world to be in her presence, no one was better rewarded then he that could best praise hir; sometimes would he (attiring him like a second *Diana* readie to chace) disguise himselfe like a shepheard, and sitting apart solitarily, where he might be in her presence, he would recount such passions as gaue certaine signes in him of an excellent wit, but matched with exceeding wickednes: among which these tenne, as the most excellent for varietie sake, after his so many villanies, I thought good to set downe in this place.

I see a new sprung sunne that shines more cleerely,
   That warmes the earth more blithly with hir brightnes
That spreads hir beams more faire, and shines more cheerly
   Then that cleere sun that glads the day with lightnes.

For but by outward heate the one offends me,
   The other burnes my bones, and melts their marrow:
The one when he sets on further blends me,
   The other ceasles makes her eie loues arrow.

From that a shower a shadow of a tree,
  A foggie mist may safely me protect,
But this through clouds and shades doth passe and perce me
  In winters frosts the others force doth flee:
But this each season shines in each respect,
  Ech where, ech houre, my hart doth plague and perce me.

This other for the strange forme therof, though it
haue the second place deserues the first, which howsoeuer you turne it backward or forward, is good sence,
and hath the rimes and cadence according, the curious-
nes and cunning whereof the learned may iudge: the
first stands is the complaint, the second the counsel;
both which he wrote in the entrance of his loue with
Diana.

Complaint.

1	3	2	*Teares, cares, wrongs, griefe feele I,*	1	1	3	2
2	2	1	*Wo, frownes, scornes, crafts nill cease,*	4	2	4	1
3	1	4	*Yeares, months, daies, howers do flie*	3	3	1	4
4	4	3	*Fro mee away flieth peace:*	2	4	2	3
		1	*Opprest I liue (alas) vnhappily,*				2
		2	*Rest is exilde, scornde, plagde, thus am I.*				1

Answere.

1	3	2	*Mend her, or change fond thought,*	1	1	3	2
2	2	1	*Minde her, then end thy minde,*	4	2	4	1
3	1	4	*Ende thee will sorrowe sought,*	3	3	1	4
4	4	3	*Kinde if thou art: too blinde,*	2	4	2	3
		1	*Such loue flie farre, lest thou perceiue and proue*				2
		2	*Much sorow, grief, care, sighing, breeds such loue.*				1

The third though short for the method, is verie sweete,
and is written in imitation of *Dolce* the *Italian*, beginning thus: *Io veggio, &c.*

> *I see with my hearts bleeding,*
> > *Thus hourely throgh my pain my life desires,*
> *I feele the flames exceeding,*
> > *That burne my heart by vndeserued fires,*
> *But whence these fires haue breeding,*
> > *I cannot finde though great are my desires.*
> > > *O miracle eterne!*
> *That thus I burne in fire, and yet my fire cannot disceern.*

The fourth being written vpon a more wanton subiect,
is farre more poeticall, and hath in it his decoram as
well as the rest.

> *When as my pale to her pure lips vnited,*
> > *(Like new fallne snow vpon the morning rose)*
> *Sucke out those sweets wherin my soule delited,*
> > *Good lord how soon dispersed were my woes!*

> *And from those gates whence comes that balmy breath,*
> > *That makes the sunne to smile when he ariseth,*
> *I drew a life subdewing neering death,*
> > *I suckt a sweete that euerie sweete compriseth.*

> *There tooke my soule his hand-fast to desire,*
> > *There chose my heart his paradise on earth,*
> *There is the heauen whereto my hopes retire,*
> > *There pleasure bred, and thence was* Cupids *birth:*
> > > *Such is their power that by a touch they seuer.*
> > > *The heart from paines that liu'd in sorrowes euer.*

An other time, at such time as in the entrance of loue he despaired of al succour, hee desperately wrote this and that verie prettely.

Euen at the brinke of sorrowes ceasles streames,
  All well-nie drownd through dalliance and disdaine,
Hoping to winne the truce in my extreames,
  To perce that marble heart where pride remaines.

I send salt teares, sad sighes, and ruthful lines,
  Firme vowes (and with these true men) my desire,
Which in his lasting sufferance scarce repines,
  To burne in ceaslesse Aetna of her ire.

All which (and yet of all, the least might serue)
  If too too weake to waken true regarde,
Vouchsafe O heauen that see how I deserue,
  Since you are neuer partiall in rewarde,
    That ere I die she may with like successe,
      Weepe, sigh, write, vow and die without redresse.

This other in the selfe like passion, but with more gouernment he wrote, which for that cause I place here consequentlie.

Heape frowne on frowne, disdaine vpon disdaine,
  Ioyne care, to care, and leaue no wrong vnwrought,
Suppose the worst, and smile at euerie paine,
  Thinke my pale lookes of enuie not of thought.

In errors maske let reasons eie be masked,
  Send out contempts to sommon death to slay me,
To all these tyrant woes tho I be tasked,
  My faith shall flourish tho these paines decay me.

And tho repyning loue to cinders burne me,
I wil be fam'de for sufferance to the laſt,
Since that in life no tedious paines could turne me,
And care my flesh, but not my faith could waſt.
    Tho after death for all this lifes diſtresse,
    My soule your endles honours shall confesse.

Another melancholy of his for the ſtrangenesse thereof deserueth to be regiſtred, and the rather, in that it is
in immitation of that excellent Poet of *Italie, Lodouico
Pascale,* in his sonnet beginning; *Tutte le telle hauean
de'l ciel l'impere.*

Those glorious lampes that heauen illuminate,
    And moſt incline to retrograde aspeɕts,
Vpon my birth-day shonde the worſt effeɕts,
    Thralling my life to moſt siniſter fate.

Where-through my selfe eſtrangde from truth a while,
    Twixt pains, and plagues, midſt torments and diſtresse,
Supposde to finde for all my ruth redresse,
    But now beliefe, nor hope, shal me beguile.

So that (my heart from ioyes exiled quite)
    Ile pine in griefe through fierce disdaines accurſt,
Scornde by the world, aliue to nought but spite:
    Hold I my tongue? i'is bad; and speake I? wurſt,
Both helpe me noughts; and if perhaps I write,
    T'is not in hope, but leſt the heart should burſt.

Another in immitation of *Martelli* hauing the right
nature of an *Italian* melancholie, I haue set down in this
place.

O shadie vales, O faire inriched meades,
 O sacred woodes, sweete fields, and rising mountaines,
O painted flowers, greene herbes, where Flora treads,
 Refresht by wanton windes, and watrie fountaines.

O all you winged queristers of woode,
 That piercht aloft your former paines report,
And strait againe recount with pleasant moode,
 Your present ioyes in sweete and seemely sort.

O all you creatures, whosoeuer thriue,
 On mother earth, in seas, by aire or fire:
More blest are you, then I here vnder sunne,
 Loue dies in me, when as he doth reuiue
In you; I perish vnder beauties ire,
 Where after stormes, windes, frosts, your life is wonne.

All other of his, hauing allusion to the name of *Diana*
and the nature of the Moone, I leaue, in that few men
are able to second the sweete conceits of *Philip du
Portes*, wose Poeticall writings being alreadie for the
most part englished, and ordinarilie in euerie mans
hands, *Arsadachus* listed not to imitate, onely these two
others which follow, being his own inuentiõ, came to
my hand, which I offer to your iudgement (Ladies) for
that afterward I meane to prosecute the historie.

Twixt reuerence and desire, how am I vexed?
 Now prone to lay ambitious handes on beautie,
Now hauing feare to my desires annexed,
 Now haled on by hope, now staid by dutie.

Emboldned thus, and ouerrulde in striuing,
  To gaine the soueraine good my heart desireth:
I liue a life, but in effect no liuing,
  Since dread subdues desire that most aspireth.

Tho must I bide the combate of extreames,
  Faine to enioy, yet fearing to offend,
Like him that striues against resisting streames,
  In hope to gaine the harbor in the end:
    Which hauen hir grace, which happy grace enioyed
    Both reuerence, and desire, are well employed.

The conclusion of all his poetrie, I shut vp with this
his Hiperbolical praise, shewing the right shape of his
dissembling nature.

Not so much borrowed beautie hath the starres,
  Not so much bright the mightie eie of day,
Not so much cleare hath Cinthia *where she warres,*
  With deathes neere neece in her blacke array.

Not so true essence haue the sacred soules,
  That from their naturall mansions are deuided,
Not so pure red hath Bacchus *in his boules,*
  As hath that face whereby my soule is guided.

Not so could art or nature if they sought,
  In curious workes themselues for to exceede,
Or second that which they at first had wrought,
  Nor so could time, or all the gods proceede,
    As to enlarge, mould, thinke, or match that frame,
    As I do honour vnder Dians *name.*

Now leaue we him in his dalliance, making all things
in a readinesse for his coronation, and returne we to the
conſtant *Margarita*, who liuing in her solitarie seate,
minding nothing but melancholies, triumphing in nothing but hir teares; finding at length, the prefixed time
of *Arsadachus* returne almoſt expired, and her impatience
so great, as shee could no longer endure his absence, in
a desperate furie setting light by her life, she resolued
priuily to flie from her fathers court to finde out *Arsadachus* in his owne countrey. For which cause she brake
with a faithfull follower of hers called *Fawnia*, by whose
assiſtance, without the knowledge of any other in the
disguise of a country maid, she gate out of the citie,
attended onely by this truſtie follower, about the shutting in of the euening, at such time as her traine without
suspect intended their other affaires, and by reason of
her melancholie little suspected her departure out of
doores: and so long shee travelled (desire guiding her
ſteps, and sorrow seating her selfe in her heart) that she
gat into an vnpeopled and huge foreſt, where meeting
with a poore shepheard, shee learned sure tidings of her
way to *Cusco*, keeping in the moſt vntrodden and vn-
frequented wayes for feare of pursute, weeping as the
walked incessantly; so that neither *Fawniaes* words, nor
the hope she had to reuisit her beloued could rid her of
ruthfulnesse: three dayes shee so walked, feeding her
thoughts on her owne wretchednesse, till on the fourth
about the breake of the day when *Phœbus* had newly
chased the morne, crowned with roses from the desired
bed of her beloued paramor, she sate her downe by a
faire fountaine, washing her blubbered face in the cleare
spring, and cooling her thirſt in the criſtal waters thereof: here had she not long reſted hir selfe, talking with

P

hir *Fawnia* in what manner she would vpbraide *Arsa-dachus* in *Cusco*, of his vnkind absence, when as sodain-lie a huge lion which was accustomed to refresh him-selfe at that spring, brake out of the thicket behinde their backes, *Fawnia* that first spied him was soone sup-prised, then she cried, and rent in peeces (in that she had tasted too much of fleshly loue) before she feared. *Margarita* that saw the massacre, sate still attending hir owne tragedie, for nothing was more welcome to hir then death, hauing lost her friend, nor nothing more expected: but see the generostie and vertue of the beast insteede of renting her limmes he sented her gar-ments, in the place of tearing her peecemeale, hee laied his head gentlie in hir lap, licking her milkewhite hand, and shewing al signes of humilitie, in steede of inhu-manitie. *Margarita* seeing this recouered hir sences, and pittifully weeping spake thus: Alas ye gods, why yeeld you sorrowes to those that despise fancie, and betray you them by death, who desire to flee detriment? wo is me, how fortunate were *Margarita*, to haue bin dismem-bred? how forlorne was *Fawnia* to be thus mangled, ah tyrant beast hadst thou spared her, her vertue had deserued it, hadst thou spoiled me, why I was reserued for it, for what care haue not I part in? or from what ioy am not I parted? Loue that is a Lord of pittie to some, is pittilesse to me, hee giueth other the rose, but me the thorne; he bestoweth wine on others, and me viniger, he crowneth the rest with lawrell in respect of their flourishing fortune, but me with Ciprus the tree dedi-cated to funerall: out alas that I liue or that I haue time to speake, I liue, in that I haue had time so long, to loue with neglect, and to pine in the delay. Ah curteous beast (said she) why executest thou not that which my

sorrow doth prosecute? let thy teeth (I beseech thee, rid
me of loues tiranny. This saide, shee pittifully wept;
but the Lion ceased not to play with her, ſtroking her
with his rough paw, as if willing to appease her, but all
was in vaine, till that sleepe by reason of her sorrow
seized her, and setled her selfe in the lions eies, where
we leaue them, returning to *Mosco*, where the day no
sooner appeared, but *Protomachus* (according to his custome comming to visite his daughter) found her sodainly fled, whereat ſtorming incessantly, he presently
put al her attendants to moſt bitter and ſtrange death,
sending out espialles through all the country to find out
Margarita, who by reason of her solitarie walkes, was
free from their search: at laſt, looking among her secret
papers, hee found a letter, wherein the princesse had
written to *Arsadachus*, that if hee presently returned
not, she would shortly visit him. By reason whereof, being a wise prince, he gathered some circumſtance of her
flight; and leuying a power of souldiers, with as much
expedition as he might, he set forward towardes *Cusco*,
where I leaue him, to returne to *Arsinous*, who ſtudying
Magicke in his melancholy cell, found by reason of the
aspect of the planets, that the houre of his reuenge was
at hand: whereuppon beeing resolued of the place,
whch was *Cusco*, and the manner, with all other actors
in the tragedie, he being desirous to behold that with
his eies which hee had long time longed for with his
hart, forsook his melancholy home, and set forward toward *Cusco*. And as he passed on his way, it was his
chance to beholde where *Margarita* lay sleeping, hauing
the lions head in her lap, whereat beng amazed and affrighted, in that he heartily loued the princesse, he with
his ſtaffe awaked her: who seeing a man so ouergrowne

in haires and yeeres; yet carrying as much shew in his
countenance, of honour, as discontent, softly ſtole from
the lion, and left him sleeping there: sodainely seasing
Arsinous by the hand, she said thus: Father, thanke fortune that hath giuen thee time to escape death if thou
liſt, and folow me, who hath both neede of thy coun-
selles, and of such a reuerend companion as thou art.
Which said, they both withdrew thẽ out of the way
haſting two long houres without euer looking backe,
till at laſt, when *Arsinous* saw her and himselfe in safetie, he courted her thus: Countrie lasse by your coate,
but courtlie dame by your countenance, whither trauel
you this waies, or for what cause are you so woful? Forlorne man by thy apparel, but honourable sir by thy
behaviour, I am trauelling to *Cusco*, where both remaineth the cause of my woe, and the means to cure it. May
I be so bold said *Arsinous* to know of you what you are,
and what you aile? It neither pertaineth to you that I
tell it (quoth *Margarita*) neither pleaseth it me to discouer it, for the one will seeke my harme, the other
yeelde you little helpe. Then quoth *Arsinous* smiling, I
will trie mine owne cunning, to crosse a womans resolution, whereupon intreating *Margarita* to set her downe
vnder a Palme tree, to auoid the heat of the sunne,
which being at his noonetide flamed very fiercely, he
drew a booke out of his bosome, and read so long til
sodainely there appeared one in selfe like shape and
subſtance as *Arsadachus* was wont to be, whome *Margarita* no sooner espied, but that she ranne fiercely towards him that haſtily fled, she cried out; Oh ſtay thee
(my *Arsadachus*) ſtay thee, behold thy *Margarita* that
hath left her fathers court, hazarded her honours, aduentured all dangers for thy loue, for thy sake, oh ſtay.

This said, the vision sodainely vanished, and she striuing to embrace him, caught his shadow: whereupon
vehemently weeping, she exclaimed on the gods, ouer
loue and his laws, renting hir haires, and beating her
breasts in such sort, as it was pittie to beholde it: and
had died in that agonie, had not *Arsinous* recomforted
hir in this sort: Fie *Margarita*, doth this beseeme your
wisdome, to demeane sorrow without cause, and seeke
your death through a delusion? why princesse whateuer
you saw was but an apparition, not the substance, deuised only by your seruant *Arsinous* to discouer you.
Shee hearing the name of *Arsinous* presently started vp,
and clasping hir armes about his aged necke, whom she
sodainly had discouered, she spake thus: Ah my father,
pardon my folly, that sought to keep that secret, which
is discouered by your science. Tut madam, the pardon
is to be granted by your hands, said he, who are most
iniured; was it euer seene (quoth he smilingly) a ladie to
bee so besotted on a shadow? Ah pardon me (said *Margarita*) I held it for the substance: but father, I pray
you tell me whither you intend your iourney? *Arsinous*
desirous in short words to satisfie her, tolde her that he
pretended his course to *Cusco*; forsaking his melancholie
cell of purpose, to meet her whose danger he had perceiued in priuate being in his studie: further he told her
many things touching the Emperours search after her,
not pretermitting any thing to content her, but con-
cealing that which tended to her ruine, which with
ernefull heart hee inwardlie perceiued, *Margarita* som-
what reioyced with the companie of such a guide, sate
her downe seeking some herbes in the forrest to releeue
her hunger, *Arsinous* that perceiued it said thus: See
madam, what loue can do, that fashioneth courtlie stom-

acks, to whomely acates the gods grant you may speede well, for I see you can feede well, hereon he opened his booke and read, and sodainely a pauilion was picht, the table was reared, the dishes serued in, with all kinde of delicates, the musicke exceeding pleasant, so that *Margarita* was rauished to behold this, but being animated by *Arsinous* she fell to her meate, certifying him at dinner time of such things as had passed in her fathers court in his absence; thus in iollitie appeased they their hungrie stomackes, and eased their sorrowfull hearts, till occasion called them forth to trauell, at which time the pauilion seruitors, and all things vanished, and onely *Arsinous* and *Margarita* were left alone, hauing two squires attending on them, with two rich gennets brauelie trapped fit for their managing, which they speedely backed, talking merrilie as they rode of such strange things as *Arsinous* had wrought by his art, and so long they trauelled towards *Cusco*, that they ariued within two leagues of the same, vnderstanding by ye great troops that rode that way, that the coronation was the next day following, *Margarita* by *Arsinous* counsaile staied in the castle of *Aged* knight, where hee wrought so by his arte, that although *Margarita* had a desire to heare tidings of *Arsadachus*, yet made she no question of him all the time of her abode there. And here let vs leaue them, and returne to *Cusco* to the accursed and abhominable tyrant *Arsadachus*, who as soone as the day beganne to breake, the birds to hale forth the sunne, the sunne to haste his course, arose from his bed, apparelling himselfe in rich and princelie robes: about which houre *Diana* was not idle, for whatso of excellence could be bought for money, or had for friendship, she wanted nothing thereof to set out her beautie: the courtiers to grace their Emperor, spared no cost, the cittizens no triumphs, so as the triumph of *Antigonus Epiphanus*, in cõparison hereof was but a trifle, the maner whereof, since it was miraculous, I haue thought good to mention in this place. First came fiue thousand of the yoongest Cuscanes out of the pallace, trotting along the streetes vnto the temple armed, according to the Roman fashion: after them as many *Tartars* armed after their maner, who were folowed with three thousand *Thracians*, and *Plessians*, all of which carried siluer lances and shieldes, hauing their headpeeces decked with ostrige plumes and emeralds: after them marched two hundred and fiftie sword-players, who followed the braue caualiers that marched before; after whom trotted the horsemen, of which one thousand, together with their horses, were all pompously garnished with golde and siluer, with a garland of gold vpon their heads: after thē rode another thousand horsemen, decked with golde and purple, with lances of golde, headed with pointed diamonds: next them rode those which were called the emperours minions, clothed in cloth of tissue, their horses trapped in greene cloth of gold, their stirrops of siluer: after them came the Emperours guard on horse backe, hauing their caparisons studded with iron and brasse, wearing vpon their armors a certain curious stoale, wherein, with gold and siluer, silke, and gossanpine threed of many colours, were woven the images of those gods, which the Cuscans most worshipped: after whome came one thousand fiue hundreth armed chariots, the most part drawn by two white genets, but fortie of them by foure: after them there came a chariot drawne by elephants, and attended by sixe and thirtie elephants, with eight hundred yong men attending them as their keepers, attired with ornaments of golde, and hauing their temples encompassed with wreathes of roses, and siluer bends: after them came eight hundred yong laddes leading many fat oxen with gilded herse to be sacrificed to the gods: next vnto them eight hundred ministers bearing platters of gold with pretious stones, vnicorns horns, and elephants teeth to be sacrificed for the health of the emperour: next which, an infinite number of statues were carried, not onely of their gods, but also of those fiends they feared; likewise the images of all their kings deceased, according as euery one de-serued for his excellence, apparelled in goodly gar-ments of golde and siluer, and other precious and in-estimable iewelles, each of them hauing a table at his feete, in which al his noble and worthy actions were written. There were likewise other semblances of the day, the night, of heauen, of the morning and mid-day, with an infinite number of vessels likewise forged out of gold and siluer, and borne by the slaues of the empire: after these came six hundred pages of the emperour apparelled in golde: after whome came three hundred virgins in white cloth of tissue, burning with censors in their handes of siluer, and *Agate* spreading sundry sorts of sweete perfumes followed by fiue hundred coches of siluer, wherein *Dianaes* damosels were carried: after which came fourescore of beaten gold, wherein all the princely heirs of the empire were royally seated. After all these the Emperour with his *Diana* rode in one coach attended with one hundred attired in beaten cloth of siluer, casting rich cloth before the coach, whereon the horses that drew the Emperour should treade. It were a vaine thing for me to set downe the riches of *Arsadachus* garments, or the attire of his goddesse: sufficeth it that it exceeded that which is past, and all was beyond beleefe: In this solemne sort entred they the temple, where (according to the custome) they were sacred, annointed and inthroned, receiuing homage of the princes. And after in selfe like pompe returned they to the pallace: where hauing many rich delicates prepared for them with sweet and melodious musike they sate them downe to eate; where, after they had somewhat refreshed their stomackes, and whetted their wittes with costly wines, *Arsadachus* remembring him of his *Margarita*, called for his box, merily iesting with *Diana*, and saying that the Empresse of *Mosco* deserued so small a remembrance, which was no sooner brought vnto him, and opened, but (see the iudgement of iust heauen) a sodain flame issued thereout, which with a hideous odour so bestraught *Arsadachus* of his senses, that thrusting the tables from him, and ouerthrowing whatsoeuer incountred him, he brake out from his seate, cursing the heauens, renting his embalmed haire, tearing his royall vestures: his nobilitie that saw this, became amazed, and among the rest, *Brasidas*, who fled for the murther in *Mosco*, and was at that time in great fauour with him, came to pacifie him; who no sooner espied him, but taking a huge boule of wine, and crying out, *Brasidas*, I drinke to *Philenia* whome thou murtheredst, he tasted the wine, and with the cup tooke him such a mighty blow on the head that he pashed out all his braines: all they that behelde this sate still; some for feare stole secretly out of his presence; among the rest, wofull *Diana* rather like the statue of *Venus* raised in *Paphos*, then the louely *Lucina* that gaue light to all *Arsadachus* delights, sate still quaking and trembling, as one readie to depart this life; whom when the Emperor espied where she sate, he haſtily ranne vnto her, crying out; Ah tyrant that haſt robbed me of my heart, my hope and life, let me sacrifice to *Nemesis*; I will sacrifice: which said, with the caruing knife he slit up the poore innocent ladies bodie, spreading her entrailes about the pallace floore, and seizing on her heart, hee tare it in peeces with his tyrannous teeth, crying, *Sic itur ad aſtra*; by this time the rumour was spread through-out the pallace, and from the pallace through the citie: by which meanes the triumphs which were commenced were turned to mournings, for *Arsadachus* vsed such cruelties euery way, that the *Numantines* for all their inhumanitie could neuer be able to match him. And in this fitte continued he for the space of sixe houres, at which time he entred the secrets of his pallace, and finding there a yong sonne which his *Diana* had bred and he begotten; he tooke it by the legges, battering out the braines thereof againſt the walles, in such sort as the beholders were amazed to see him; this done he flung it on the ground among the dead members of his mother, calling on the name of *Artosogon* and *Lelia* his father and mother, and telling them, that in some part he had yeelded them reuenge. By this time *Arsinous* and *Margarita* were entred the citie, who hearing the tur-moile thorow the citie, queſtioned the cause thereof, and were certified by those that passed by, in what eſtate the emperour was at that present. *Margarita* hear-ing the cause, beganne wofully to exclaime, til she was pacified by *Arsinous*, who told hir that the nature of the medicine which he gaue her, was such, that if *Arsada-chus* were conſtant to her, it would increase his affec-tion; if false, it would procure madnesse: to which effect, since the matter was brought, it coulde not be

but the yoong Emperour had wronged her. With these
perswasions hee drew her to the pallace, where thruſt-
ing through the prease *Arsinous* thought himselfe happy
to see such a reuenge wrought on his enemie. *Margarita*
was heartlesse to behold the dolefull eſtate of *Arsadachus*, so that forgetting the honor of his name, and the
modeſtie of her sex, she brake thorow the guard, and
ranne to *Arsadachus*, where he sate embrewed in the
bloud of innocents, and with teares spake thus vnto
him; Is this the ioy of my loue (said she) are these thy
welcomes to thy beloued in ſteede of triumphes to feaſt
her with tragedies, in lieu of banquets, with blood? why
speaketh not my deare spouse? why lookeſt thou so
ghaſtly? O if it bee thy pleasure to shew crueltie on me,
make it short by a death, not lingering by life. *Arsadachus*
all this while sate mute gaſtly ſtaring on *Margarita*; at laſt
fiercely flinging her from his necke, his rage reuiued and
he cried out; *Diana*, ah *Diana* by thy bright lookes, by
thy beautifull lockes, let not thy ghoſt be displeased,
thou shalt haue bloud for bloud, here is the sacrifice,
here is the inſtrument; wherevpon drawing a rapier out
of the sheath of one of those who miniſtred faſt by
him, he ranne *Margarita* quite thorow the bodie: and in
this sort with bedlam madnesse fled out of the presence
to his privy chamber. The poor princesse euen when
death beganne to arreſt her, pursued him: and as she
indeuoured to vtter hir moanes, fell downe dead on the
floore; whom *Arsinous* wofully bewept, and in the presence of the princesse of *Cusco*, discouered what she was.
Then beganne each of them to imagine a new feare,
doubting leſt the Emperour of *Mosco* should reuenge
her death at their handes. For which cause they con-
sulted how to shut vp *Arsadachus* til *Protomachus* were

certified, which they effected sodainely, in that they found him laide on his bed, and soundly sleeping, enforced thereunto by the industrie and art of *Arsinous*. Who after he perceiued the whole assembly of princes dismayed, caused the ministers to gather vp the mangled members and couer thē with a rich cloth of gold, and afterwards seeing al the courtiers attentiue, he beganne in this manner: *Thales* (ye worthie princes) after he had trauelled long time, and at last returned home, being asked what strange or rare thing hee had seene in his voiage, answered; an olde tyrant: for certaine it is, that such as practise open wrong, liue not long; for the gods yeeld them shortest life that haue the wickedest wayes: muse not therefore to see your yong Emperour in these passions, whose sinnes if they be ripped vp exceede al sence, whose tyrannies surpasse the beleefe of any, but such as haue tried them. What, know you not of his disobedience, who spared not his owne father that begate him, his deere mother that bred him? What, knowe you not of his periurie? that hath falsified his faith to *Protomachus*, betraied and murthered *Margarita*, and at one time frustrated the hope of both these empires? What, know you not of his murthers, where these in sight are sufficient to conuict him: but those I sigh for are more odious, who thorow his lewd lust bereft me (poore *Arsinous*) of my daughter, and her of an husband? But the iust gods haue suffered me to behold the reuenge with mine eies, which I haue long wished for with my heart. Truely (yee *Cuscans*) ye are not to maruell at these chaunces, if you bee wise, neither to wonder at your emperours troubles, if you haue discretion; for as vnitie (according to *Pythagoras*) is the father of number, so is vice the originall of many sorows. When the fish *Tenthis* appeareth aboue the water, there foloweth a tempest: when euils are growne to head, there must needely follow punishment; for as the gods in mercie delay, so at last in iustice they punish. Heare me yee men of *Cusco*, and consider my words, if neuer as yet any tyrant liued without his tragedie what should you expect? In faith no other thing but the confirmation of *Platoes* reason, who saide that it is vnnecessarie for him to liue, that hath not learned how to liue well. The tyrant of *Sicely Dionisius*, (of whome it is said, that he gaue as great rewarde to those that inuented vices, as Rome did to those that conquered realmes) died a priuate man and in miserie. Nowe what in respect of this man can you hope of *Arsadachus*, who hired not men to inuent, but did himselfe in person practise: beleeue me, beleeue me, your sufferance of such a viper in your realme, is a hainous sinne in you; and as *Dion* saith, it is but meete they be partakers to the paine, who haue wincked at the fault. *Caligula* the emperor of Rome was so disordered in his life, that if all the Romanes had not watched to take life from him, he would haue waited to take life from them; this monster bare a brooch of gold in his cap, wherin was written this sentence: *Vtinam omnis populus vnam præcise ceruicem haberet, vt vno actu omnes necarem.* And what was this man in regarde of *Arsadachus*? Truely almost innocent; for the one pretended kindnesse to those that gently perswaded him, but the other neither feared the gods, neither spared his friends, neither regarded iustice, and can such a monster deserue life? The Romanes when the tyrant *Tiberius* was made away, sacrificed in their open streetes, in that the gods had reft them of such a troublesome wretch; why cease

you then (you *Cuscans*) to sacrifice to your gods, to the
end they may deliuer you of this troubled world. It was
a lawe among the Romanes, that that childe which had
disobeyed his father, robbed any temple, iniured any
widdowe, committed any treason to a stranger should
be banished from Rome, and disinherited of his fathers
possessions; and what hath not *Arsadachus* done of
these things? and why is not *Arsadachus* punished? *Sce-
dasus* daughters being violated in *Lacedemon*, and vn-
reuenged by the magistrates of the cittie; the gods
afflicted both the guiltie and vnguiltie with plagues,
in that they afflicted not punishment on the offenders:
and what can you hope (ye *Cuscans*) that suffer this
sincke of sinne to triumph in your pallaces? You will
perhappes say, that no man is to be punished afore hee
be conuicted. And (I pray you) for what should ill men
pleade? since as *Chrisippus* saith, nothing is profitable
vnto them. You see testimonies of his murther before
your eies, tokens of his periury I ring in your eares, his
lust the gods abhorre, and shall he yet liue?

This said, there grew a great muttering among the
nobilitie, and the noise thereof awaked the emperour
(whose sleep had stayed the working of the inchant-
ment) who finding himselfe wholy imbrewed with
blood, his doores fast locked vnto him, beganne to
misdeeme: whereuppon calling and exclaiming on his
attendants, some of them at last fearefully opened the
doores. The nobilitie hearing of his freedome, presently
fled; but when as the fatall fruits of his furie were discouered vnto him, and his ruthfull eies beheld what
his hands had executed, Lord what pittifull exclama-
tions vsed he! how hee rent his breast with furie, how
he tare his face: At last, laying him downe vpon the

mangled members of *Diana*, and embracing the dead
bodie of *Margarita*, hee washed both of them in his
teares, and demeaned himselfe so wofully, as it was
wonder to behold; at laſt, with a bitter sigh he brake
out into these bitter words, (whileſt his nobles hearing
of his recouery, beganne to reenter the pallace) True
it is that *Plutarch* saith (quoth he) that life is a ſtage-
play, which euen vnto the laſt act hath no decoram: life
is replenished with al vices, and empouerished of all
vertue. Sooth spake *Chrisippus* when he alleadged this,
that the euilles of this life are so many, that the gods can
not inuent more, neither a liuing man indure halfe; so
that rightly I may say with *Hercules*:

> *Plenus malorum sum iam, nec supereſt locus*
> *Alijs nouis recipiandis————*

But why philosophie I of life complaining on it
where I ought onely to conuict my selfe? It is not the
wretchednesse, but the wickednesse of life that maketh
it odious. Then haſt thou occasion (wretched man) as
thou arte to learne thee, who hauing sinned in the
excesse, oughteſt rightly to haue thy comforts in defect.
Yea I haue sinned O ye heauens, firſt in beguiling this
chaſt *Margarita* with hope, in wronging my deere
parents in their age, in slaughtering this poore infant
with his mother. Oh *Aetna* of miseries that I see! oh ye
Cuscan princes, why suffer you me aliue, that haue
ſtained your empire with such infamies? why vnsheath
you not your swords? for pitie delay not, for pittie rid
me of life: alas, why craue I pittie, that haue beene altogether pittilesse? ah yee flockes of flatterers, where are
you nowe that fedde me with follies? come nowe and
punish my follies in me: none heareth me, all forsake

me, despised of the gods, hated of men; al. iuſt heauens, I honour you that haue left mee occasions in my selfe, you cursed eies of mine that haue glutted your selues in vanitie, since you reft me of my senses, I will be re-uenged on your sight: which saide, hee drew out his eies weeping piteously in so erneful maner, that the whole assiſtance became compassionate: at laſt some one of his nobles labouring to pacifie him, alleadging reasons of great weight, which in a man of gouernement were sufficient to quallifie the furie of sorrow, he replied thus: Friends and princes the force of reason, (as the Stoicks say) is not to bee vsed in those things that are not, it concerneth not me (lords) that I liue, perswade me not for that cause to entertaine and thinke of life, for if it be odious to those that through infirmities of their flesh grow in hate with it, what should it be to me, who haue not onely a bodie aggreeued with sorrowes, but a soule sweltered in sinnes; lament mee not there-fore, neither releeue me; for as the dewe causeth lepro-sie in man though it yeeldeth life to floures, so teares rather torment those that dispaire then releeue them; and though they comfort the diſtressed, yet they are tedious to the desperate: I feele my forlorne heart (you nobles) cloyed with thoughtes and longing to be dis-burthened. I see with mine inward eies the ghoſts of these poore slaughtered soules calling for iuſtice at my hands; ſtay me not therefore from death, but assiſt me to die, for by this meanes you shall ridde your countrey of a plague, the world of a monſter. Such as are wound-ed with brasen weapons, are according to *Ariſtotles* opinion soone healed; so likewise are they that are taunted with easie sorrow: but whereas the passions ex-ceede reason, they haue no issue but death; the inſtrument that woundeth is deadly. Ah my heart, I finde *Plutarchs* reason of force; for as the sunne is to the heauen, so is the heart to the man; and as the one eclips-eth, the other cloudeth; when the one danceth, the other dieth. I feele thee (poore heart) dispossest of al ioy, and shal I continue possest of life? no (you ghosts) I will visit you. This saide, he grapled about the floore among the dead bodies, and at last he griped that weapon where-with he slew *Margarita*, wherewith piercing his hated bodie he breathed his last, to the generall benefit of a the *Cuscans*, who in that they would pacifie the emper-our *Protomachus*, who as they vnderstoode had leuied a huge armie after they had enterred their slaine em-perour with his faire loue, bestowed honourable funer-all on the princesse *Margarita*, on whose sepulchre, as also on that of *Dianaes*, *Arsinous* wrote these epitaphs.

Margaritaes Epitaph.

A blessed soule from earthly prison losed,
*   Ye happie heuens hath faith to you conuaide,*
The earthly holde within this tombe inclosed,
*   White Marble stones within your wombe is laide:*
The fame of her that soule and bodie lost,
*   Suruiues from th'ile to the Bractrian coast.*

A precious pearle in name, a pearle in nature,
*   Too kinde in loue vnto too fierce a foe,*
By him she lou'd, shee dide, O cursed creature,
*   To quite true faith with furious murther so!*
*   But vaine are teares for those whom death hath slaine,*
*   And sweete is fame that makes dead liue againe.*

Q

Dianaes Epitaph.

Thy babe and thou by fire and husbands hand,
  Belou'd in ſtaied sence was slaine in rage,
Both by vntimely death in natiue land
    Loſt Empire, hope, and died in timelesse age,
      And he whose sword your bloud with furie spilt,
      Bereft himselfe of life through cursed guilt.

All ye that fixe your eies vpon this tombe,
  Remember this, that beautie fadeth faſt,
That honours are enthralde to haples dombe,
    That life hath nothing sure, but soone doth waſt;
      So liue you then, that when your yeares are fled,
      Your glories may suruiue when you are dead.

In this sort were these murthered princes both buried, and honored with epitaphs, by which time the
emperor of *Mosco* arriued in *Cusco*, who certified of that
which had insued, with bitter teares lamented his
daughter, and vpon the earneſt submission of the *Cuscans*, spoiled not their confines, but possessing himselfe
of the empire, he placed *Arsinous* gouernor of the same,
whom vpon the earneſt reconcilement and motion of
the Princes, he tooke to fauour, being certified of his
wrong and innocencie: which done, he returned to
Mosco, there spending the remnant of his
dayes in continuall complaints of his
Margarita.

FINIS.

NOTES

MENAPHON

3. 11. Euphues censure to Philautus] *Euphues his censure to Philautus* was written by Greene shortly before *Menaphon*. Philautus is the forlorn lover and Camilla the fair disdainful maid of Lyly's *Euphues and his England*, the sequel to *Euphues*. Neither of Greene's books have any connection with *Euphues*; the names are added for their advertisement value. Lodge, also to claim a connection with *Euphues*, calls his *Rosalynde* 'Euphues' golden legacy, found after his death in his cell at Silexedra.'

4. 1. *To the Gentlemen Students of both Vniversities*.] For a full discussion of this preface see *The Works of Thomas Nashe*, edited by Dr. R. B. McKerrow (especially vol. iv, pp. 444-459).

4. 10. *placet*] approval.

4. 25. art-masters] experts.

5. 1. kilcow conceipt] bombastic idea.

5. 10. take vp a commodity] raise a loan.

5. 26. extemporall vaine] Nashe much admired Greene's rapidity in writing. In *Strange Newes* (McKerrow, i, 287) he says, 'In a night and a day would he have yarkt up a Pamphlet as well as in seaven yeare.'

7. 12. Gothamists] Wise men of Gotham, i.e. fools.,

7. 16. punies] freshmen.

7. 18. furmentie] frumenty.

7. 33. what doo you lacke] the shopman's cry to the passers-by.

8. 2. crepundios] idle talkers.

8. 8. friplers] frippers, old clothes dealers.

8. 22. table] picture. 'The table of the world turned vpside down' is the sign of an inn.

8. 28. It is a cōmon practise now a daies] This famous passage is the chief evidence for the existence of a pre-Shakesperean *Hamlet* written by Thomas Kyd. The arguments in favour of the interpretation are set forth in Dr. F. S. Boas' edition of *The Works of Thomas Kyd* (p. xlv); Dr. McKerrow, however, disagrees (iv, 449).

8. 33. necke-verse] the passage (usually the first verse of the 51st psalm) which a condemned man had to read to claim benefit of clergy.

11. 22. to vaunt the pride of contraction in euerie manuarie action] i.e. to take pride in manuals (manuaries) epitomising learned works rather than in the works themselves.

11. 23. *Pater noster* . . . in compasse of a pennie] This feat of penmanship was performed by Peter Bales, author of *The Writing Schoolmaster*.

15. 1. vndermeale] afternoon.

18. 6. *Abcie*] Absey or ABC book, a card containing the alphabet, the Lord's Prayer, etc., used for the beginner's first reading lessons. It is often called the horn book, being mounted on a wooden handle covered with horn to guard it against the schoolboy's hard handling.

18. 11. my *Anatomie of Absurdities*] Nashes' *Anatomy of Absurditie* was entered at Stationer's Hall on September 19, 1588.

18. 16. *Paules*] St. Paul's churchyard was chiefly inhabited by booksellers.

19. 11. *a* Lillie] i.e. John Lyly who set the fashion of 'labouring beautie' with his *Euphues* (1579).

19. 14. *Greener obiectes*] puns on Greene's name are tediously common in the works of his admirers, and of his enemies. R.B., for instance, in *Greenes Funeralls*, 1594, begins his ninth sonnet—

> Greene, *is the pleasing Obiect of an eie:*
> Greene, *pleasde the eies of all that lookt vppon him:*
> Greene, *is the ground of euerie Painters die:*
> Greene, *gaue the ground, to all that wrote vpon him.*

23. 2. quiddities] subtleties.

23. 28. *Laualtos*] lavolta, a high-stepping dance.

24. 8. champion] champagne, open country.

25. 4. *Chrisocolla*] borax or green earth.

37. 5 posset] a hot drink made of milk curdled with wine.

39. 10. *desiune*] dejeuner.

39. 13. chamlet] camlet, an Eastern fabric.

40. 10. deined her eyes] noticed.

40. 13. cruell] worsted.

40. 19. cintfoyle] cinqfoil.

43. 11. polt-footed] clubfooted.

44. 32. bottles] wicker baskets.

45. 5. conceipts] imaginings.

46. 24. beauties of:] Mr. Percy Simpson in his *Shakespearian Punctuation* (p. 71) notes the regular use of a colon to mark interrupted speech.

47. 5. Hobbie] an inferior breed of hawk.

47. 20. crost me] retorted.

48. 2. rammage] wild.

48. 27. cracke] break.

50. 4. amate] astonish.

50. 11. cassock] long coat, usually used for the soldier's great-coat.

50. 25. pad] food.

51. 19. girded] cut—as with a whip.
       frump] contemptuous remark.

51. 22. impreso] device, motto.

51. 23. frowes] women.

52. 15. Saturnists] morose dullards.

52. 16. quatted] satiated.

54. 19. leekes] 'She says men die for love *when* larks die from leeks, id est, never' (Grosart).

57. 29. Epitazis] the development of the plot.

58. 25. *Heliotropion*] the heliotrope
       load] attraction, i.e. the sun.

61. 16. haute] high.

62. 7. sowterly] like a cobbler.

62. 32. pheare] fere, mate.

65. 12. nine holes] a country game in which the players had to roll the ball into holes, scoring on the principle of bagatelle.
66. 23. Hodge] peasant.
71. 22. *Non est inuentus*] i.e. the letter could not be delivered.
71. 30. affie] trust.
74. 6. kistrell] a hawk of base breed and so unreliable.
75. 6. *Tyre*] prey.
76. 13. newe change driuen you to a night cap] The Elizabethan invalid used to tie his head up in a kercher. So in *Julius Cæsar* (II, i, 315) Brutus says to Ligarius,

> 'O, what a time have you chose out, brave Caius,
> To wear a kerchief. Would you were not sick.'

77. 26. kercher] cloth.
80. 9. pannicles] skull.
80. 11. fauchon] falchion.
83. 28. hansell] the first money taken at market; so, first use.
85. 15. platted] plotted.
90. 27. woones] dwells.
92. 17. whist] silenced.
92. 19. moderne] commonplace.
93. 15. stowre] encounter.
95. 21. rustie bills] The bill had gone out of use as a weapon, though it was still carried by the watch.
98. 3. difference] the addition or alteration made in a coat of arms to denote the younger branch of a family.

A MARGARITE OF AMERICA.

113. 4. *M. Candish*] Thomas Cavendish began his unfortunate voyage to the Straits of Magellan with three tall ships and two barks on August 26, 1591. The expedition was a failure from the first; Cavendish's own crew mutinied, and on May 20, 1592, the fleet was scattered. Cavendish died at sea, leaving a letter wherein he bitterly denounced John Davies for having deserted him. The miserable story can be read in Hakluyt.
115. 18. curets] cuirasses.
115. 23. shot as gards to the pikes] in military diagrams of the period, the pikes are shown as marching into action in close formation with the more mobile harquebusiers surrounding them in open order.
116. 23. the whole confines and reuenewes whereof is not sufficient to acquit for one moneth of your charges] compare Hamlet's outburst (IV, iv, 58).
117. 14. If you will be held vertuous and monarchies] The text should probably read 'if you will be held vertuous monarchies,'
monarchies] monarchs.
120. 21. An infant first from nources teat he sucketh] Compare Jaques
> 'At first the infant,
> Mewling and puking in the nurse's arms' . . .
> *As You Like It*, II, vii, 143.)

127. 4. dolie] doleful.

129. 1. burgend] budded, fresh grown.

129. 23. emet] ant.

130. 2. Thou art leauing thy country for an other court] Compare the whole passage with Polonius' advice to Laertes, *Hamlet*, I, iii, 57.

131. 24. opinion] good repute.

138. 25. I must ende with &c.] I must leave what follows to your imagination.

146. 30. rescouse] rescue.

151. 30. hemd are each supposes] if the reading is correct the phrase should probably be paraphrased, 'coughed away is every kindly thought.' For this use of 'hem,' compare *As You Like It*, I, iii, 18:
    'These burs are in my heart.' 'Hem them away.'

154. 1. vnicorns horne.] A piece of 'genuine' unicorn's horn was one of the treasures of Windsor Castle shown to the Duke of Wirtemberg on his visit there on August 20, 1592 (Rye, *England as seen by strangers*, p. 16).

154. 18. sendall] a fine cyprus silk.

154. 31. after good] subsequent happiness.

160. 25. that the poore deceased ghostes may be appeased] The ghost of a murdered man could only be appeased by the violent death of the murderer. In the *Hystorie of Hamblet* (translated from the Belleforest's version of the Hamlet story), Hamblet, having slain his uncle, says: 'This just and violent death is a just reward for such as thou art: now go thy wayes, and when thou commest in hell, see thou forget not to tell thy brother (whom thou trayterously slewst) that it was his sonne sent thee thither with the message, to the ende that beeing comforted thereby, his soule may rest among the blessed spirits, and quit mee of the obligation that bound me to pursue his vengeance upon mine owne blood. . . .' (Gollancz, *The Sources of Hamlet*, p. 257.)

163. 10. *pease*] pea.

164. 15. The original punctuation has been left, but the sense would be improved by reading a full stop at *drownd* ', and continuing

> *Showers cherish*
> *Thy barren bosome in the field:*
> *I perish*
> *Since nothing may me comfort yeelde.*

166. 29. his mistresse fauour, which was a sleeue of salamanders skinne] The sleeve was detachable and often worn by a knight as a token of his lady's love. In *Troilus and Cressida* Troilus gave Cressida a sleeve as a parting gift, which afterwards she gave to Diomede.

173. 3. limning] painting; but here, 'outlining'.

173. 17. *incipe*] the command given to a disputant in an academic exercise to begin his argument.

178. 21. wrings] turnings.

189. 7. *Aperse*] A per se, A 1, the one and only.

189. 10. carkanets] necklaces.

191. 18. boade] abide.

198. 24. yongman] 'young man' and 'boy' (like the modern 'pup') were both used as terms of insult meaning insolent and inexperienced.

200. 25. nouelties] revolution. 'Innovation' is often used with the same meaning.

204. 15. pale] literally fence; here used for the mouth as in the Homeric phrase ἕρκος ὀδόντων, the pale of the teeth.

210. 11. generositie] nobility.

210. 11. but see the generositie and vertue of the beast] The lion being a kingly beast recognised the true princess by instinct. By the same instinct Falstaff sensed Prince Hal in the dark on Gadshill.

213. 29. ernefull] yearning, forboding.

214. 1. whomely acates] homely fare.

219. 3. prease] press, crowd.

TEXTUAL NOTES

MENAPHON

THE original texts of these romances have been repro-
duced in this edition without alteration, except that the
roman type has been used for the black letter, the tall 'f'
printed 's', and the '&' as 'and'.

The text of *Menaphon* has been printed from a copy of the
first edition in the British Museum; in this copy the last leaf of
Nashe's preface is missing, and has been supplied from the Bod-
leian copy of the second edition.

A few misprints have been corrected, viz.:—

8. 8. after *for the original reading* afetr
16. 6. *Celiano,* for *Celiano.*
16. 24. tutchstone *for* tutcsthone
21. 6. resolution, *for* resolution.
24. 24. *Anacreon* for *Auarreon*
26. 20. continue *for* coutinue
39. 16. chamber *for* chauber
52. 20. shepheards *for* shepheads
59. 27. *vaunts* for *vauuts*
66. 27. *Pleusidippus* for *Pseusidippus*
96. 31. *Democles* for *Damocles*
103. 2. *did,* for *did.*
104. 17. *was.* for *was*

A MARGARITE OF AMERICA

The text of *A Margarite of America* is taken from a copy of
the first edition in the British Museum. It is very faulty, and the
punctuation is exceedingly haphazard; this, says Lodge, was because the printer was not acquainted with his hand and the book
printed in his absence.

The following corrections have been made:—

116. 6. these *for* their
120. 8. with *for* which

127. 12. *long,* for *long.*
129. 6. as *for* (as

129. 13. hir *for* his
134. 20. vngracious *for* vegracious
135. 2. *Minecius* for *Minecins*
143. 8. help *for* belp
146. 3. you *for* yon
146. 20. flint) *for* flint;
148. 16. toombe *for* toobme
150. 1. coruption *for* cornption
151. 11. yet *for* ye
153. 25. court, *for* court(
157. 20. *Arsadachus*) for *Arsadachus*
163. 2. *caue* for *care*
163. 10. *pease*, for *pease*.

163. 16. *neglect*, for *neglect*.
164. 20. *daunt*, for *daunt*.
172.25. their *for* theie
175. 20. (I *for* I
180. 31. *dachus* for *dachns*
181. 18. in *for* im
191. 25. *Cosco*. for *Cosco*
194. 1. plentifull, *for* plentifullmy
194. 21. weaknesse, *for* weaknesse
206. 6. *confesse*. for *confesse*
211. 1. thee, *for* thee
211. 13. *Margarita*, for *Margarita*.
214. 27. *Arsadachus* for *Arsadachns*